THE WORK, pleasure, and well-being of everyone living on the surface of this planet are continually determined by atmospheric processes. For more than twenty years, Florence van Straten has probed the atmosphere for its secrets and she gives a vivid account of the excitement of this exploration in a career devoted to atmospheric research and development.

As a member of the United States Navy, she saw how the remnants of our Pacific fleet were able to seek sanctuary in the protective covering of a cold front following their daring strike on the Gilbert and Marshall Islands less than two months after the attack on Pearl Harbor, and she describes the nature of such a front. There is discussion of weather forecasts with

ıade in remote parts of
in the atmosphere, by
balloon, and weather sat-
ʼith tailored forecasts for
he behavior of tornadoes,
typhoons is described
ysterious reactions to the
Although weather is a
re is truth in the ancient
ch are presented, antici-
al theory of weather de-
edures for collecting data
are described along with international co-operation for sharing information. The author portrays as well her own experiments in modifying and controlling weather; the making and prevention of rain, with its perils and advantages, and the infanticide of hurricanes. With this fascinating variety of information on the weather, illustrated by diagrams and drawings, Dr. van Straten not only makes the talking about it more interesting but indicates the extent to which something may be done about it.

Weather or Not

WEATHER OR NOT

Florence W. van Straten

Illustrated with
Photographs and Diagrams

DODD, MEAD & COMPANY · NEW YORK

Library of Congress Catalog Card Number: 66-20447
Printed in the United States of America

Acknowledgment for the illustrations indicated is made to the following:
U.S. Navy, pages 30, 36, 38, 43, 73, 74, 186, 206, 207, 211
ESSA, pages 34, 117, 165 166, 170, 174, 176
Winzen Research Inc., pages 47, 48
Weatherwise, pages 78, 82
Whitney Gallery of Western Art, Cody, Wyoming, page 97

In Loving Memory of
J. v. S. and R. v. S.

Preface

Two kinds of discussion and interchange of ideas count greatly in the pleasures I experience. One sends me repeatedly to scientific meetings dealing with research and development in fields in which I specialize, where time passes unnoticed as my confreres and I present, debate, argue details of our work using terminologies, equations, and concepts that would be meaningless to people outside our very special little province of scientific investigation.

Equally, however, I enjoy listening to someone who specializes in a field other than my own—scientific, literary, philosophic—when he tells me of his subject in terms that I can understand. If he is able to convey the elements of his specialty in such a way that I do not feel that I am getting the elementary course prerequisite to advanced study, I live happily for a time in a new and wonderfully different world.

I am satisfied to devote my energies to my own work and have no desire to be an amateur endocrinologist, minerologist, or dermatologist. Yet, my curiosity is gratified when someone tells me about his work, what it encompasses, the kinds of problems encountered, and the various techniques employed in finding solutions. If, as a result, I receive some inkling of the fascination that my companion discovers in the work he does, I feel as privileged as though I had been presented with a rare and precious gift. Indeed, I have then received just such a gift.

For more than twenty years, I have probed the atmosphere and participated in various atmospheric studies. This exploration has been exciting and stimulating. Since the work, pleasure, and well-being of everyone living on the surface of this planet are continually determined by atmospheric processes, my field of study must be of general interest, and I want to tell about it.

In the telling, I am not trying to create a new set of amateur or professional weathermen. Any knowledge of atmospheric phenomena gained will not serve as a substitute for Meteorology I at a university. Here is no survey course. Indeed, my objective is quite the opposite. I am not lecturing in an undefined classroom, but chatting over a coffee cup or a glass of beer.

During the course of our conversation, some important aspects of weather science will be skipped because it so happened that I was never concerned with them; others will perhaps be overemphasized because I have devoted long years to them. Some of the material has been simplified because the detail is of interest only to the professional.

If this book conveys some understanding of how it is possible for a very small fraction of the population to devote its time and energy, eagerly and happily, to atmospheric studies and weather forecasting, it will have served its purpose.

F. v. S.

Washington, D.C.

Contents

	Preface	vii
1.	The Weather Matters	1
2.	Seen from a Distance	22
3.	Balloons and Ballunatics	40
4.	Atmospheric Explosions	55
5.	Is Our Climate Changing?	76
6.	The Wind Doth Blow	88
7.	Weather Lore and Science	101
8.	Battles of the Air	116
9.	In a Fog	134
10.	Weather on the Air	157
11.	The Weather Observer's Lot	169
12.	Making and Breaking Clouds	187
13.	Goals and Dreams	213
14.	Meteorology Must Grow Up	225
	Index	231

Illustrations

The Sun Heats the Earth Unevenly 4
A Cold Front Moves Toward Pearl Harbor, February 1942 9
Aircraft Carriers Use a Wave on the Equatorial Front To Hit Rabaul 14
Wind and Ship's Course for Aircraft Take-off and Landing 14
A Radar Pulse (r-f Energy) Finds a Target 28
Cold Front on a Radarscope 30
Thunderstorms on an Iso-echo Contour Radar 34
Five Showers Fall from a Large Cloud as Seen on a Vertically-Scanning Radar 36
How the Bright Band Forms 37
Bright Band on a Height-Finding Radar 38
One Type of Radiosonde for Measuring Pressure, Temperature, and Humidity Aloft 43
Inflation of a Constant-Altitude Balloon 47
Constant-Altitude Balloon at the Moment of Release 48
Wind Speeds and Their Equivalents 59
Annual Frequency of Tropical Storms 60
Winds about a Hurricane 61
Paths of Some September Hurricanes 62
Atmospheric Pressure Changes as a Hurricane Passes Martinique, August 8 - 9, 1903 63

Swell Leaves the Storm Area 64
A Hurricane as Seen on Radar 73
Free-Floating Buoy Automatic Weather Station 74
Mean Winter Temperatures at New Haven, Connecticut 78
Mean Snowfall in Central Maine 78
Frequency of Atlantic Hurricanes 79
Frequency of Hurricanes Striking Florida 79
Frequency of Hurricanes Striking New England 79
Temperature Changes Through the Ages 82
Global Circulation 91
The Sea Breeze 93
The Land Breeze 94
The Valley Wind 95
"Waiting for a Chinook" 97
Zones of Audibility and Silence for an Explosion 110
A Sound Beam Bends 112
Bending of a Radar Beam 113
Development of a Radar Hole 114
A Cold Air Mass Spills over the Plain States 117
Cross Section of a Cold Front 119
Cross Section of a Warm Front 121
Typical Frontal Profiles 123
Weather Analysis Symbols 124
Stability of Lifted Air 128
Weather Map Produced by Electronic Computer 165
Conventional Weather Map with Satellite Input 166
Interior of an Instrument Shelter 170
Tipping-Bucket Rain Gauge 172
A Wind Speed Record 174
Maximum and Minimum Thermometers 176
Mercury Barometer 176
Stormy Sky 180
Cloud Forms
Cirrus 181
Cirrocumulus 181

Cirrostratus 182
Cirrus and Cirrostratus 182
Altocumulus 183
Altostratus 183
Altostratus and Stratocumulus 184
Altocumulus and Stratus 185
Cumulus 186
Cumulonimbus 186
Vapor Pressure over Ice and Water 203
Dissipation of a Cloud 206
Man-made Clouds 211

Weather or Not

1

The Weather Matters

The date was January 1942, and the United States was in the midst of two wars. The first had just started the month before; the other had been raging longer than the memory of man, long before the first tiny glob of protoplasm had reproduced itself and so could be called a living cell. The second war was the one that raged in the atmosphere. In January 1942, the United States Navy used a battle in the one conflict to bring victory to a skirmish in the other.

On the surface of the earth in the mid-Pacific, two task forces approached the atolls of the Gilbert and Marshall Islands held by the Japanese. The cloudless sky and unlimited visibility permitted planes from the task-force carriers to attack the islands' installations almost continually. In short order, one Japanese transport was sunk and nine other ships badly damaged in the lagoon. Planes, hangars, and supply dumps were effectively bombed and strafed while the Japanese atoll commander was killed along with some of his men.

During the early afternoon, some hours after the morning attack, the Japanese recovered sufficiently from their surprise to launch two ineffective bombing attacks on the aircraft carrier *Enterprise* which formed the heart of one of the task forces.

The seagoing plane at that time was no match in speed, maneuverability, or fire power for the land-based craft. Discretion dictated that our forces should retire. But where to? It would take two days of steaming at full speed to get beyond the range of the Japanese bombers. The fate of the U. S. Navy and of our country—perhaps the fate of the world—depended upon our naval forces finding shelter from the Japanese bombers.

This was the end of January 1942. Geared as we are now to the strength and might of our navy with its task forces stretching ships from horizon to horizon, it is difficult to think back to the time when a handful of ships leaving the Gilbert and Marshall Islands at full speed represented the major remnant of the Pacific Fleet. The rest formed a junkyard around Ford Island in Hawaii.

At the beginning of World War II, the strength of a naval force was measured by the number of its battleships. But within a few hours on the seventh day of December 1941, the Japanese had eliminated seven of our great battlewagons from combat. Sixteen "Kate" torpedo bombers flying at forty to one hundred feet above the water, accompanied by "Val" dive bombers, using both bombs and armor-piercing shells, dropped their deadly payloads on our ships. They completed the devastation by circling about immediately to strafe personnel already working courageously to restore the watertight integrity of their ships. Within twenty minutes of the beginning of the attack, the battleship *Oklahoma* rolled over in its berth. The *Maryland*, alongside, took two direct bomb hits while the *West Virginia* took not only two bombs but six or seven torpedoes as well. The *Tennessee,* bombed and fire-ravaged, faired slightly better. She survived sufficiently to make it back to the West Coast after jury repairs and was able, toward the end of the war, to rejoin the fight.

The story of the *Arizona* is too well-known to warrant retelling here. Her remains in the waters of Pearl Harbor, now a national shrine, still provide silent testimony to the 1,103 officers and men who lost their lives on her. With solemn ceremony and before the eyes of residents and tourists, her colors are still raised and lowered each day.

The *California* and the *Nevada* complete the list of battleships sorely wounded on December 7, 1941. Through the gallant action and brilliant seamanship of their crews, they were both reparable and, after complete and lengthy West Coast overhaul, able to fight the latter half of the war.

Destruction of the smaller units of the U. S. Fleet was proportionately complete and the list of casualties too numerous to detail. Newspapers asked during the last month of 1941, "Where is the U. S. Pacific Fleet?" Official Washington did not offer an answer. Only the enemy could be comforted by the confirmation that a large part of it was sunk or so damaged as to be useless.

The saving grace, probably recognized by only a few naval officers of the "brown-shoe" variety, was the unscathed survival of the three aircraft carriers in the Pacific. While, even now, there is a considerable difference of opinion between the "airdales," the naval aviators who wear brown shoes, and the surface naval officers, known as the black-shoe navy, as to the relative merits of air versus surface warfare in strategy and tactics, in 1941 there was little argument: the value of the carrier was totally unestablished. Now, twenty-odd years later, we believe that we fared better losing the seven battleships than had the three carriers been lost, but in 1941, many would have preferred reversed casualties.

At any rate, the only punch left for either offense or defense was represented by the three aircraft carriers. And what did the country do with its last remaining weapons in the Pacific? Move them out of danger until others could augment and support them? Hold them in readiness should the Japanese threaten to invade the West Coast?

No, indeed! The giant had been all but felled; but battered, bleeding, bewildered, he had not lain supine. He was striking back, not in blind rage but with desperate cunning. The United States, all but fatally wounded at Pearl Harbor, was not defeated. Our country was not yet ready to trade body blows with the enemy, but it was on its toes, jabbing skillfully to keep its foe off balance and wary.

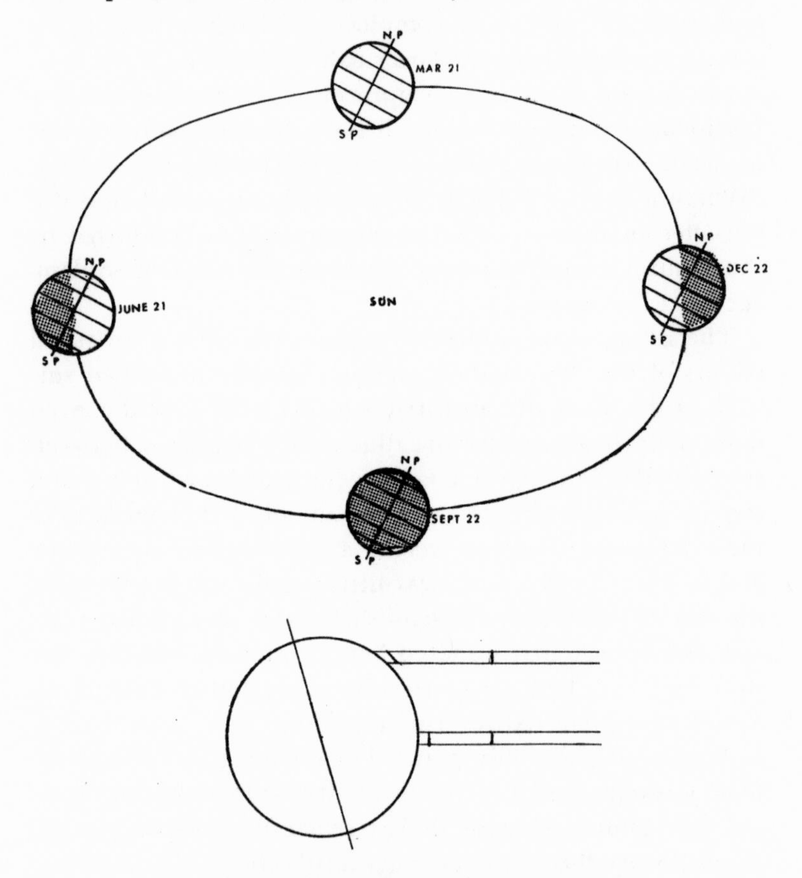

The Sun Heats the Earth Unevenly

Unbelievably, it had risked its last few resources, its last ounce of energy, in an offensive attack on an enemy stronghold. The United States struck at the Gilbert and Marshall Islands one month and twenty-four days after the attack on Pearl Harbor.

However, now it seemed the moment of reckoning was upon us. The task force, mission accomplished, was fleeing the seemingly inevitable, disastrous counterattack of the Japanese.

It was now time for the concurrent war, that in the atmosphere, to play its decisive role. A weather officer aboard the carrier *Enterprise* was canny enough to recognize that the small force of which he was a part could be lost to view if it sought out the battle front marking the struggle between two giant natural forces: polar air and tropical air, which fight unceasingly in a warfare as real, although not always as deadly, as a war fought by man.

There, ninety-three million miles away, is not only the giver of life but also the warlord who started the atmospheric battle when the earth was first born and has kept the fight raging with undiminished fury ever since: the sun. On every square centimeter of the atmosphere in the tropics, it pours its two calories of solar energy every minute of each daylight hour. The rest of the earth's envelope it favors with but a glancing puff of heat, save the winter pole, which it ignores entirely. Warmer and warmer becomes the air near the thermal equator and colder and colder, relatively, becomes the polar air. It is a struggle between the have-nots and the haves.

"I'll have some of that nice heat, thank you," says the underprivileged air near the poles as it rushes toward the equator to displace the overheated moist air boiling up there. It forms a great tide at the surface pushing down hungrily to partake of the life-giving warmth.

"O.K. with me," answers the equatorial atmosphere. "I

have too much of a good thing anyway." Lightheaded from the heat and humidity, it rises and obligingly starts its way poleward as a great river of warm air aloft counterbalancing the corresponding stream of cold air at the surface. Fortunately or unfortunately—the point is debatable—the two great rivers do not manage to flow in this equalizing manner as on a well-regulated automobile throughway. Three forces over which the streams have no control spoil the neat traffic pattern. The first involves the physical obstacles that interrupt the free flow: mountain ranges, continents, hot deserts, and cold plateaus generate whirls and eddies disrupting the north-south currents.

The second disturbance results from the inherent characteristics of the tropical air itself. Stormily it rises near the equator; filled with its own inner fire, it starts making its way poleward; but, as with its turbulent human counterparts, the fury is soon dissipated, and the hot fire quickly extinguished. As the air rises, it expands and cools. Moving toward the pole, it gets farther and farther away from its source of heat supply and, reaching regions of the atmosphere that make greater demands on its ability to give off warmth, it loses its early initiative and sinks disconsolately back to the surface. There, it is met by the stream of cold air coming from the pole. The war between warmer air and colder air is on. The beachhead is taken and the mobile front established.

The collision between hot and cold is not usually head on. No blitzkrieg, this. The third force is in operation, parrying the blows, causing them to glance off, largely negating the entire effort to achieve the desired balance between the "haves" and "have-nots" of heat. A third force? Yes. The force resulting from the spinning of the earth on its axis, called the Coriolis force.

It is as though the cold air at the north pole takes careful aim at New York City's Empire State Building and rushes like a missile toward its target. But the world turns beneath it. As it moves along what it thought was the straight-line trajectory, the Empire State is no longer before it. Pennsylvania, Ohio, and Indiana replace it in the sights. Long before it reaches the latitude of New York, it seems to have turned at right angles to its original course. Straight as an arrow it seemed to fly, but the spin of the earth apparently shoved it to the right, and what started as a cold river flowing from north to south winds up as a stream flowing from east to west.

The northbound tropical air meets a similar but opposite fate. At the equator, on the bulge of this earth of ours, it is spinning more rapidly than its northern target. As it travels northward, the earth below it seems to lag behind, and the warm river is also turned to the right, eventually flowing from west to east.

The interminable war is on. As long as the sun distributes its blessing inequitably, as long as the world rotates on its axis, the heat balance will not be achieved. The hot and cold will fight it out in the middle latitudes with first one getting the upper hand and then the other, while humans witnessing the battle keep score with blazoning headlines: "Heat Wave Enters Sixth Day" reports *The New York Times* in August. "Record Cold In Northeast" exults the *Miami Herald* in two-inch letters across page one on a December day.

It was to a cold front in the mid-Pacific that the weather officer on the *Enterprise* looked that day when the U. S. Navy was trying to escape the retaliatory wrath of the Japanese. Seen from a satellite, if one had been orbiting at that date, the cold front would have looked like a thin white ribbon stretching approximately fifteen hundred miles in a northeast-southwest arc. On each successive orbit, the satellite would have observed that the entire configuration was moving eastward although the orientation of the ribbon remained unchanged.

No satellite report guided the *Enterprise* weather officer, but he read his weather maps correctly and knew Pacific air-mass behavior. He knew a great blunt wedge of cool air was shoving its way under the warm, moist air in its path, forcing this air not so much to retreat as to seek higher altitude to override the on-coming surge. The warm, moist tropical air forced upward, cooled and could no longer support its cargo of water vapor. Great drops of water condensed, forming a line of clouds and rain for a thirty-mile swath outlining the cold front.

The weather officer told his skipper of the natural smoke screen and suggested that the task force use it for shelter. By steering a northerly course at high speed through a cloudless and moonlit night, the *Enterprise* and her escorts encountered the cold front at about 0800 the next morning. Fortunately, the Japanese planes had lost contact with the ships during the night and were unable to take advantage of the excellent flying weather marking the initial phase of the retirement.

Once in the frontal zone, light continuous rain, a ceiling of about three hundred feet and visibility between one-half and two miles made flying conditions undesirable. The orientation of the front and its eastward movement permitted the ships to steer a constant northeasterly course (065°) and by adjusting the speed to that of the front, the task force could travel both northward and eastward, eventually reaching Pearl Harbor without leaving the protective embrace of the clouds and rain.

Throughout the forenoon and afternoon of the first day following the attack, enemy planes were known to be only about twenty miles to the south on courses paralleling the front but, apparently, the enemy pilots never attempted flight through the line of towering cumulus clouds. In all probability, even if they had been more daring, such a ma-

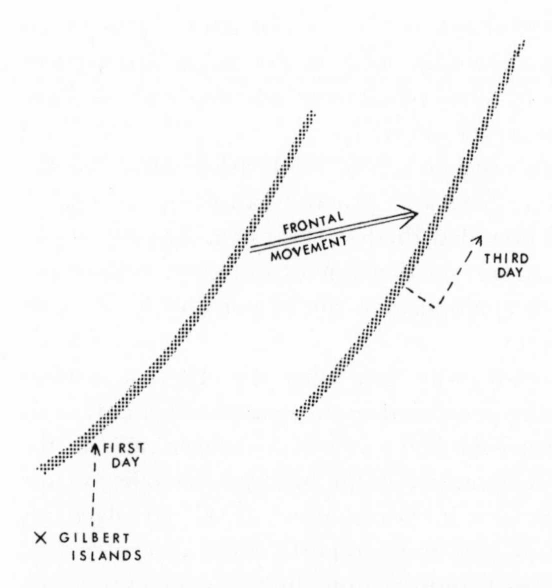

"Show Me the Way to Go Home." A Cold Front Moves toward Pearl Harbor, February 1942.

neuver would not have been successful since the very poor visibility made efficient scouting impossible.

An occasional slight change of course to conform to the small undulations in the cold front kept the task force within its protective belt. No planes could be flown from the carrier and topside personnel got very wet. These were the only inconveniences suffered by the Americans.

Finally, on the night of 2 to 3 February, the Task Force Commander decided that the ships were out of range of Japanese patrols. He ordered a southeasterly course for a short time, taking the task force out and ahead of the front into the region of clear weather with unlimited ceiling and visibility. Off the port beam, the front remained, the horizontal column of "smoke," guiding the force to safety in much the same way that the column of smoke by day led the Israelites across the desert in their escape from Egypt, as reported in Exodus. A simple order to the helmsman to steer by remaining thirty miles off the line of clouds would have guaranteed a satisfactory landfall.

Only on the morning of arrival off Pearl Harbor did the front pass over the ships and proceed eastward, its services no longer needed now that the force was nearing port. It was as though the front, proud that one of our carrier forces accepted its protection, undertook the responsibility of showing it the way home.

There are not many who remember the effect of weather on the success of the first carrier raid against the enemy. I do because I had joined the Navy as a Wave officer early in the war and my first assignment at the headquarter office of the Naval Weather Service in Washington, D. C., involved my reading war diaries and battle reports while reconstructing weather maps so that I could analyze the use made of weather.

The Naval Weather Service was an organization created around the time of World War I. It had eked out a precarious and minimal life during the period between the two wars, serving uninterested aviators who in that era flew mostly by the "seat of their pants."

With the onset of World War II, as aircraft became more sophisticated and operations spread to two oceans, the organization grew apace. The Director of the Naval Weather Service believed, however, that weather information was vital not only to the aviation arm but to all aspects of naval operations. He had studied his history carefully and well. From earliest recorded times, long before the beginning of the Christian era, the outcome of military and naval engagements had depended to a considerable extent on weather and its elements. This account could start with the parting of the Red Sea before the Israelites, although the Director usually started rather later. He could talk of the Greek defeat of the Persians in the waters around Salamis during the Persian wars and of the winds that, more effectively than the English, destroyed the Spanish Armada. He spoke graphically of the weather gauge and its significance to the maneuvers of the privateers and sloops of the American revolution and the Napoleonic wars. He knew in detail the weather factors influencing the outcome of the Battles of Jutland and of the Falkland Islands, where Sir Frederick Sturdee destroyed a German squadron under the command of Graf Maximilian von Spee in 1914. He was not certain, however, that the current crop of naval commanders had been educated to use weather as a weapon against the enemy.

He conceived the idea of preparing a series of reports of the early World War II engagements to show how weather had been used cleverly and to advantage or ignored to our detriment with loss of life and ships. He wanted each such report to be concluded by a section entitled "Lessons Learned" in which, sparing no feelings and "taking his finger off his number"—an expression signifying that he was ignoring any consequences to his career advancement—he would distribute kudos and boos appropriately to friend and foe. Each American naval commander would get his copy and would, hopefully, react intelligently.

In the report I wrote of the raid on the Gilbert and Marshalls, needless to say, the task force commander received a great big plus for his canny use of weather. With my stripe-and-a-half rank placing me in the lower echelons of the Navy, I was all for giving the plus to the weather officer who shared my lowly status, but the Navy does not operate that way. The admiral received the plaudits.

The Pacific war diaries and battle reports for the remainder of 1942 produced many more analyses demonstrating both intelligent and careless use of environmental factors. In the Battle of the Coral Sea, the American forces made good use of the equatorial front during the first few days, sinking a Japanese carrier, the *Shoho,* in ten minutes. "Scratch one flattop!" was the immortal message signaled by the dive-bomber pilot. Many Japanese aircraft were shot down, and the Land of the Rising Sun lost six more planes when, in the poor weather, they mistook the American carrier, *Yorktown,* for their own mother ship and landed on her. Another Japanese carrier was seriously damaged during those first days when our ships stayed under the front. Our losses amounted to two oilers, ships of the train, which dutifully stayed away from the combat area and sat out in the open away from the frontal zone. During the last days of the engagement, for some inexplicable reason, the Japanese and Americans exchanged position and thereby reversed scores; our ships left the protective cover of the cloud band while the Japanese moved under the natural shelter. We lost the carrier, *Lexington,* the beloved "Lady Lex." Verbal pats on the back as well as blows on another anatomical feature were accorded the task force commander for that battle.

The original landings on Guadalcanal were timed to coincide with a violent cold front leaving Australia for the Solomon Islands. Our forces merely followed the front and attacked just as it rolled away from the entrenched Japanese forces. The enemy apparently did not realize how narrow the zone of bad weather was. It seemed inconceivable that an attack in force could be launched when the wind was so strong, driving huge tropical raindrops like bullets into man and weapons alike. During such a storm, it is sensible to cover all equipment and take shelter.

Our grade school history books tell the story of General

Washington's Christmas Eve victory over the Hessian mercenaries at Trenton attributing it to the inability of the British hirelings to conceive of anyone attacking on such a night; they spent the holiday eve feasting and drinking instead of preparing for a revolutionist's onslaught. The difference between the enemy at Trenton and on Guadalcanal was a matter of physical comfort prior to the attack. The nature and the effect of the surprise was the same, however: The Hessians were defeated, and the Japanese were unable to offer any resistance for two days following the first landing.

Afterwards, the struggle for Guadalcanal turned bloody and became one of the more difficult and arduous actions of the war in the Pacific; but without the two days of grace during which American men and supplies could be landed on the beachhead without harassment, our forces might have been pushed off the island immediately, and the course of the war might have been significantly changed.

One of the most interesting actions of the early part of the war actually had little military significance but represents an almost classic textbook case of using weather as an ally. The action is known officially as the November 5, 1943 air strike at Rabaul on New Guinea, but all who engaged in it give it a subtitle, "Angel Riding on the Yardarm," quoting the observation of one of the ship's crew following the attack.

Militarily, that and subsequent air attacks on Rabaul were planned to protect our landing on southwestern Bougainville. As in all such carrier-aircraft attacks on fixed island installations, the odds were always against the carrier planes. Although now, with catapult launchings from carrier decks, faster, heavier, high-performance naval aircraft can be used which are a match for any other planes, this was not true during World War II. The carrier aircraft then might well have displayed a sign saying "Don't shoot! I'm just a poor, sitting duck." Land-based aircraft could and did fly circles

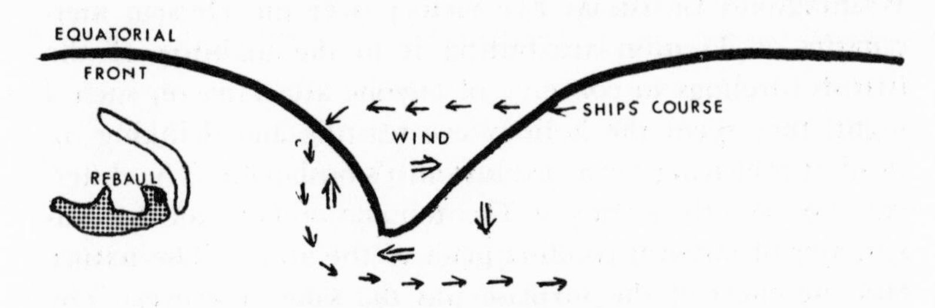

"Angel Riding the Yardarm." Aircraft Carriers Use a Wave on the Equatorial Front to Hit Rabaul.

around the lumbering creations with their collapsible wings and beefed-up undercarriages, slow take-off and landing speeds and, more importantly, low cruising speed and poor maneuverability.

To be successful, a naval air attack had to be of overwhelming strength or catch the enemy unaware. Since the range of land planes exceeded that of carrier-based craft by a great deal, if the entire force were to escape a punishing counterattack, it had to escape the notice of the enemy. The "angel riding the yardarm" in the attack on Rabaul set the stage for this particular scene of the drama of war precisely in a way favoring the American force.

The thermal equator hovered in the vicinity of the flight path. Along this line, winds from the southern hemisphere

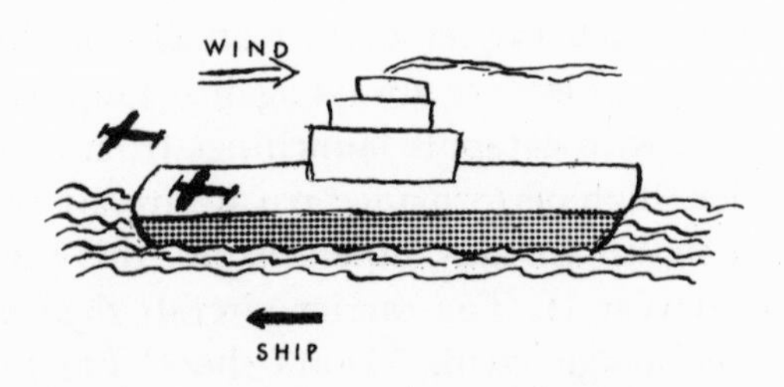

Wind and Ship's Course for Aircraft Take-off and Landing

meet those from the northern, creating neither a cold front nor a warm front, since the temperature in the tropics is too uniform; but an equatorial, or intertropical, front, marked usually by a general cloudiness and a wind shift. On this front, a small wave, or perturbation, had formed where a small outcropping of northern-hemisphere air had pushed just a little farther south than its neighboring air. Around the little wave, the winds blew in a roughly circular pattern, just a bit stronger than elsewhere along the front, and in a clockwise direction because the weather system was in the southern hemisphere. Clouds around the wave were a little higher and thicker than elsewhere.

Miraculously, the wave was not only on the direct route to Rabaul but also at the right distance from that target so that the carrier aircraft with their limited fuel supply could just make the round trip. Steadily, the aircraft carriers steamed toward the target on the northern side of the wave, into the wind, not only adding the wind speed to their own velocity through the water to permit aircraft launching off the bow but also reducing the distance the planes would have to fly. To get the greatest advantage from the wind for take-off, the ships did not have to deviate one iota from their set course toward the target.

Only after the attack aircraft were winging to the west did the carriers swerve, carefully staying within the cloud limits of the wave formation, but moving first south and then eastward. The relatively high overcast and the low scattered clouds typical of a wave disturbance on the intertropical front prevented detection by enemy scouts without hampering our pilots in their flight from and to the mother ships.

Rabaul, to the west of the disturbance, was in the clear—unlimited ceiling and visibility—and our attacking planes could execute a classic bombing and strafing exercise. Despite the limited number of planes participating and their limited payload capacity, Rabaul got clobbered that November 5th.

After the attack, the planes returned to their carriers, which were now streaking for "home" but which were also exactly oriented to receive their planes with the wind again blowing over the bow.

By way of contrast, a week later another strike was scheduled using not only the ships and aircraft of the first attack but sufficient additional forces to increase the strength threefold. During the week, the intertropical front had oscillated, of course, and this time the target was in the cloudy frontal zone while the carriers were in the clear. The first difficulty encountered was the matter of getting the planes airborne. The winds were too light and the speed the carriers could develop as a substitute was almost insufficient to permit launching.

Problem two revealed itself when the planes approached the target area: Simpson Harbor on Rabaul, with its Japanese ships, was so hidden by clouds that our planes could not locate it. Not one hit was scored in the harbor. The only bright note during this useless exercise was the absence of enemy aircraft near our carriers, which could have found no place to hide in case of attack.

It was fun, at first, digging out the facts of the various engagements from the war diaries and reconstructing the action and the weather. As the months rolled by, however, two things soured me on these analyses. First, as we recovered our strength and augmented our forces, the encounters with the enemy became more complicated and less clear-cut with respect to weather effects. Massive numbers and overwhelming strength usually carried the day.

Second, the Director of the Naval Weather Service showed increasing reluctance to place the blame on the line. Perhaps he had been ordered to "cease and desist," or perhaps, with an ever-increasing weather organization under his command, he started having visions about broad stripes—that promotion from captain to admiral that ranks above the elixir of youth, fame, fortune, or the hope for eternal salvation as a goal for military men. At any rate, the kudos were made more fulsome and the boos were so revised as to become all but inaudible. I finally revealed my evaluation of this philosophy by submitting an action analysis ending: "Lessons Learned. It ain't the heat. It's the humidity."

He got the message. The analysis was returned to me for publication with a revised "Lesson Learned" and a note attached: "See me."

"What job would you like?" that wonderful man asked when I went to his office.

"Research and development," I answered.

"O.K. Report to the R. and D. section tomorrow."

So I was through preparing the operational analyses and began a career in research and development in the atmosphere. But I have never quite gotten over the wonder of the role that weather plays in our lives—not only for military purposes but also in civilian pursuits.

To most of us, weather seems significant only when we plan some outdoor activity. The picnic will be pleasant only if the sun is shining brightly, and the trip to the beach is successful only under similar conditions. Monday morning washday, for those without clothes dryers, also requires sparkling weather, and the housewife on that day will scan the horizon as keenly as any windjammer captain before her.

Not everyone wants good weather all the time, of course. The farmer needs his quota of rain, and even city dwellers, with lowered reservoirs and rationed water following a prolonged drought, wish for rain—for a few hours, at least. I received my comeuppance once when I cheerfully told some prospective duck hunters that the next day would be just perfect: not a cloud in the sky, seasonable temperature, and light winds. How was I to know that ducks have all the advantage under such conditions? I found out soon enough after making my enthusiastic pronouncement.

The farmer and the baseball fan, the hunter and the picnicker, the fisherman and the housewife are at odds about perfect weather and should weather control ever become feasible, it will be difficult—impossible, rather—to satisfy all simultaneously.

For most of us with indoor chores, central heating systems, and air conditioners, weather seems significant only on rare occasions, and unsuitable weather seems at most a minor inconvenience. Actually, the elements that make up weather play a large part in our lives. Police blotters in summer reflect the outside temperature, with the crime rate rising with the temperature and humidity to a point. On the broiling hot days, the crime rate drops again. Apparently, the dog days of August enervate even the most determined thug. When we are born and when we die also seem to be weather-dependent. At least, there are those who find a correlation between the atmospheric pressure—the barometer reading—and both the time of entry and exit from this world. A doctor in charge of the maternity ward at one of the naval hospitals, where the wives of personnel had their babies, would call the weather office for a weekend pressure forecast each Friday during the latter part of World War II. Of course, he may have been a crank, but he believed that when high pressure dominated the area more women would come to term than if low pressure prevailed. He allotted weekend passes to doctors, nurses, and corpsmen accordingly.

Another doctor, not in the Navy, claims that more people die about 4 A.M. than at any other time during a twenty-four hour period. Meteorologists and atmospheric physicists know that the atmospheric tide is always lowest at four o'clock in the morning. Low pressure, according to these statistics, may loosen the bonds with which we cling to life. Personally, I have not examined these data, and, moreover, I am aware that statistics are like a bikini: revealing what is fascinating and concealing what is vital. I will not vouch for these conclusions; I will assert, however, that weather affects our lives in all manner of interesting and unrealized ways.

For a few, weather and its vagaries play a direct role in a way not usually considered by the many. There is a small grocery store, for example, located on the fringe of a sizable city at the intersection of two major bus routes: one coming from the heart of the city and the other going toward suburbia. The owner has a contract with a commercial weather forecaster who provides him with rain predictions consisting of time of onset, amount of precipitation, and duration. The grocer ties in his orders for bread and milk from the wholesaler with the forecast. He has learned that if it starts to rain in the middle of the day suburban wives call their husbands in town to tell them to pick up a loaf of bread and a bottle of milk on the way home. The freezer and the pantry will provide the rest of the family meals until the wife can drive her station wagon to the supermarket under more propitious circumstances. And what is more logical than that the husband drops into the little grocery between buses at the transfer point? At any rate, this grocer believes that using weather forecasts to determine his milk- and bread-stock level pays him a sufficient profit to offset the cost of the special service.

Many communities in the northeast also contract for specially tailored forecasts during the winter months in order to provide maximum snow-removal service at minimum cost. Will it snow during the night? If so, it would be well to have the day crew station snow-removal equipment at strategic locations the day before—at single-pay rates rather than at the time and a half for overtime tariff. Will the snowfall be followed by an immediate thaw? Perhaps snow removal will not be necessary at all, or, at the very least, sanding and salting can be avoided; or perhaps only the major arteries will have to be cleared and lesser thoroughfares will take care of themselves.

Various public and private utilities often require and use tailored forecasts as well. The number of degree-days is a well-established index that defines the coldness of winter. Oil deliveries and natural-gas storage requirements for heating are a function of the degree-day total. If the deliveries for the one and the amount of stored gas for the other can be timed to meet consumer demands, a considerable amount of money can be saved.

The requirements of the electric power plants are perhaps even more closely geared to the immediate weather. How much electricity will be used in the area serviced by the power plant? The goal is to produce just enough kilowatts and no more. Too many are wasteful while too few can be disastrous, shutting off electric appliances within the entire area. Just think of the effect of a summer-afternoon thunderstorm. The sun disappears behind the tremendous cloud and an untimely dusk pervades the community. In home and office, light after light is snapped on. The first few drops of rain begin to fall and are soon followed by a hard, pelting, wind-driven torrent. In those places where air-conditioning equipment has not already been draining electrical energy, windows are slammed down and electric fans are switched on.

Too little available power? Blackout! With a good forecast of an unusual peak-power requirement, the electric utilities can take care of the community in such a way that Mr. and Mrs. Consumer remain totally unaware of the silent service accorded them.

This kind of weather prediction is called a tailored forecast, and it is worth explaining what is meant by the term and describing how it differs from an ordinary forecast. The usual weather information gives a general weather picture describing the state of the sky—clear, partially cloudy, or cloudy—the maximum temperature, the minimum temperature, and the prediction of precipitation—chance of afternoon or evening showers. For many purposes, this is sufficient information for planning activities and garb.

The tailored forecast is usually geared to only one weather element, attempting to predict that element accurately with respect to time and quantity. If the state of the sky is not important to the situation, forget it. Concentrate only on the vital weather element. If you are pouring concrete during the fall or winter months, temperature is important. Not any temperature; actually, only one value matters: 32°F, the freezing point of water. If the temperature is above that, concrete can be poured successfully. If the temperature will fall below that value during the hardening period, concrete should not be poured. The tailored forecast is simply: will the temperature fall below 32°F during the vital period.

Interestingly enough, the forecaster can do a better job in predicting one weather element precisely than in giving a general or qualitative prediction of a number of elements. Because he concentrates on only one aspect of the weather map, he usually can achieve greater accuracy.

2

Seen from a Distance

The meteorologist's dream—the perfect forecast! To know from minute to minute, today, tomorrow, next month, next year what the weather will be. However dull life may become when the elements no longer offer any surprises, those men and women concerned with improving weather science exert every effort toward developing the ability to predict atmospheric conditions precisely.

How does the scientist begin to realize that dream? The materials he works with stagger the imagination. He is trying to chart the behavior of a gaseous envelope surrounding the earth, which weighs approximately 5,700,000,000,000,000 tons, extending from the surface some several hundred miles into space where it peters out so gradually that no boundary can be established. From a great distance, the sun drenches it with heat energy in a constantly changing pattern as day follows night and season follows season. Cosmic radiation from farther reaches bombards the rarefied gases, rearranging molecular patterns, while the gravity of earth, moon, and sun interact, pulling the gaseous envelope out of shape in a complex tidal flow.

Where land and air meet, every surface roughness interrupts the smooth interplay of the other forces. A heavy patch of vegetation, a forest clearing, a mountain range, a coral island emerging through the ocean surface break up established streamlines. Forest fires, factory smokestacks, erupting volcanoes introduce contaminants into the atmosphere, which change the amount of heat the air absorbs from the sun and provide a moving web trapping the water in the air to form clouds. And each cloud generates its own little circulation within the larger one: tiny eddies within a giant whirlpool.

The air rests not only on the land but also on the ocean—mostly on the ocean, since four-fifths of the earth is covered by water. Here, two great mobile fluid masses interact so that cause and effect become completely merged. The wind increases, and the water becomes more turbulent, which in turn increases the friction of air against water and produces a drag in the lowest portion of the atmosphere. From the ruffled surface, more water vapor pours into the disturbing air. Little ripples grow into breaking waves splashing great drops of salty water upward, where some of the water evaporates and the salt is carried along invisibly as yet another cargo influencing the weather processes in places near and far.

A jet aircraft streaks across the sky, a comet pulling its tail of condensed vapor exhaust behind it. Most often, the white plume evaporates quickly, serving only momentarily to guide the eye of a casual observer or an antiaircraft gunner to the metallic speck at its source. But, very occasionally, the air is so close to saturation, or so unstable, that the plane, with its fuel exhaust, triggers a profound change. The condensation trail, white in the clear blue sky, not only does not disappear, it grows and spreads, serving as a germ cell from which develops a cloud cover tenting over hundreds of square miles. The solar energy no longer bakes the ground below. Evaporation from lakes and rivers and from vegetation is diminished. The atmospheric processes are altered locally, and the effect is felt in an ever-increasing arc downstream.

Would the cloud cover have developed in any case even had the jet plane not crossed the sky? Perhaps. Or again, perhaps not.

If all the millions of persistent factors influencing the atmosphere were known and their relation to weather understood sufficiently to permit computation, it would still be necessary to take into account the accidentals: the man-made influences, such as plane flights, irrigation projects, factories, and forest fires, as well as the cosmic events, such as sporadic solar flares and meteoric showers.

With the advent of the electronic computer, a small beginning has been made in the preparation of a weather forecast by computation, but mainly, the meteorologist has tried to solve his immediate forecast problem by improved observations. He believes that his best hope for prediction in the near future lies in the ability to see what is happening about him and to use his experience and intuition in projecting the current situation forward a few hours at a time.

By far the greatest emphasis in meteorological research and development has been placed on the effort to project the observer's eyes to the greatest distance possible. The observer has long been accustomed to making his hourly trip to his instruments to read the temperature, humidity, wind speed and direction, and barometric pressure, stopping off at the rain gauge to record the amount of rainfall accumulated, while gazing about him to note the visibility and the amount, kind, and height of cloud. Much of the research has been geared to making these same measurements for him automatically at remote, unpopulated locations on the earth's surface or high in the atmosphere where he cannot reach directly.

The second aspect of the research and development struggle has been to try to see the weather picture as a whole, as though the observer were on a high movable mountain peak from which he could scan the skies around him. Radar and the weather satellite have been the principal tools developed for this purpose.

When I first transferred to the R. and D. section of the Naval Weather Service, radar's usefulness had just been discovered and adaptation for meteorological purposes constituted the major part of my first assignment there.

I cannot remember when I first heard of radar. It was not available to the combatants at the beginning of the war, but later, it made its way to all the war theaters with great rapidity. I did not entirely take in the real impact of radar on the war, until the European phase was over and the Germans had surrendered—not only their weapons and military forces but also their war diaries. During the summer of 1945, these diaries appeared in Washington, providing all of us at the Navy Department with the most fascinating reading matter.

During the first few years of the war, the U-boat captains recorded nothing but a series of triumphs. Their words were quietly official, but the tone was clearly jubilant. They roamed the surface of the Atlantic in packs, seeking out convoys of allied cargo and passenger vessels. Then they submerged to launch their deadly torpedoes at the foe. Life for the submariners was a breeze. Often, they enjoyed long hours in the sunshine during the day, and always at night they were exposed to the atmospheric oxygen. The story told in each of the diaries was always the same: great mobility on the surface followed by an occasional dive that invariably resulted in one or more kills to be transmitted to Kiel, Bremerhaven, and Berlin.

Then, gradually, their periods of movement on the surface became shorter and shorter as aircraft, subchasers, blimps, or destroyers so often appeared over the horizon necessitating a quick dive to escape discovery. The frequency of depth-charge attacks over their positions increased, and the attacks were made with ever greater accuracy. Not only were the U-boats forced to move slowly under water, using battery power, and the crews compelled to live on impure air in yellow, artificial light, but also the success of their torpedo runs on the lumbering convoys was considerably reduced. To top it all, reporting U-boat captains noted with increasing frequency the loss of contact with other U-boats in their hunter-killer packs. These subs they were forced to consider lost. It seemed as though the Allied anti-submarine forces knew where the U-boats were operating.

One by one, the diarists comment on the possibility that the Allies had acquired some new secret weapon that could see through the darkness and report range and direction. The conjectures about the secret weapon were stated in fanciful terms at first. It almost seemed a joke, but as the months progressed and U-boat warfare increasingly became a losing proposition, the humor hidden under the official language of the diaries disappeared. One after the other, the German captains reached the certain, sober conclusion that the Allies had just such a device as radar.

All of that was much later. In the beginning, although I had nothing whatsoever to do with the development of radar as a means for detecting and tracking ships and aircraft, I did get very involved with using this new tool for weather detection and analysis.

We received many reports from our ship commanders—complaints, rather—that enemy aircraft tracked by radar would merge into an almost static blob on the screen and be lost from view. These slow-moving, irregular blobs were identified as echoes from clouds. The aircraft would take shelter in a fat, dark cloud and disappear from sight both visually and on the radar screen. Radar operators demanded that something be done to get rid of these undesirable weather echoes so that they could get on with their business.

Undesirable! 'Tis an ill wind, etc. We in the weather field looked at the echoes and found an answer to our prayers. Radar could serve us as well as the other military interests. It permitted us to extend our vision a hundred or more miles to see weather patterns developing as they approached our point of observation.

Perhaps I should explain. Radar, the acronym stands for *ra*dio *d*etecting *a*nd *r*anging, is equipment capable of performing three functions: it can transmit a packet of radio energy, it can receive a packet of energy, and it can measure time in terms of a millionth of a second. Essentially, the radar emits a tiny blast of radio energy in the direction in which the antenna is pointed. It then turns off its transmitter and switches on its receiver. The little bundle of radio energy sweeps out into space. If it fails to find anything in its path, it just keeps going, diminishing in intensity with distance as the energy is spread through a larger and larger volume. In the meantime, the receiver just stands by. After a period of listening, measured in infinitesimal fractions of a second, the receiver switches off, the antenna turns microscopically, and the transmitter sends another parcel of energy into the atmosphere at a slightly different angle.

Suppose, however, in its radiating pattern outward, the tiny burst of energy intercepts an airplane. The solid metallic frame of the aircraft serves as a mirror, reflecting the packet of radio waves. Some small part of the reflected wave returns to the antenna and is detected by the open receiver. "I sense something," says the receiver. "Exactly 1/1000 second between the time of transmission and the time of reception," says the timer. "Aha," clicks the computer. "A radio wave travels 186 miles in 1/1000 second. Figuring half the time for the trip out and half for the trip back, the object is exactly 93 miles away." On a scope, at a distance equivalent to 93 miles

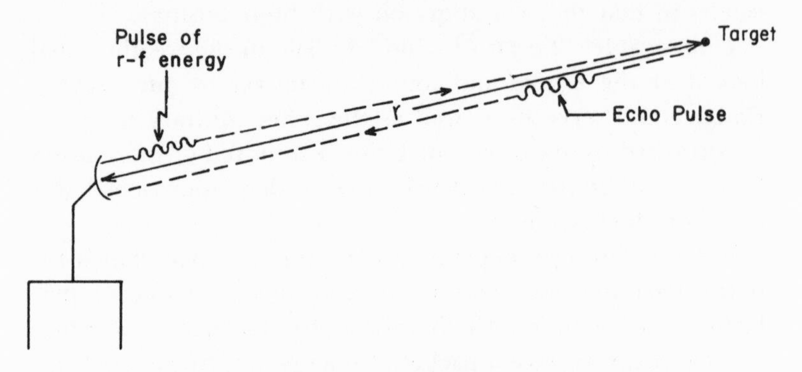

A Radar Pulse (r-f Energy) Finds a Target

and in a direction corresponding to the direction of the antenna, a little spot appears. There is the echo produced by the target.

Essentially, only "hard" targets can be "seen" by radar—objects that can do a good job of reflecting radio energy. Metal is a good reflector while wood and human beings are not. Radar is blind to the last two. But there is a whole range of reflectivities from very poor to excellent for various substances, and a really good radar operator can see all manner of qualities in the returned echo. Often he can identify the nature of the target by these qualities. Characteristically, this skill is translated into "he can see the captain tying his shoelaces on the bridge" in giving the final accolade to the skill of the gifted operator.

A raindrop is not a hard target, of course, and reflects almost none of the radar transmission. Yet in a large cloud, there are countless raindrops, and while the echoing by one droplet is infinitesimal, the myriad of droplets multiply to give the infinitesimal dimension. Thus, a precipitating cloud can give a fairly solid radar echo so that a plane's echo can merge into it and be lost.

The way in which a number of insignificant echoes can combine to give a solid one results occasionally in some fantastic phenomena. Years later, in the 1950's, when much more was known about radar and the atmosphere, an observer in Texas noticed that early each morning, on a certain spot on his scope, a small, bright circle formed. Gradually, the circle expanded forming an ever-increasing ring that progressively became weaker and weaker as it grew until it disappeared from view. Near sundown the process reversed. Apparently out of nothing, a tenuous ring appeared and gradually became smaller and smaller as well as brighter and brighter on the scope, until it became compact. It then promptly disappeared from sight.

Innumerable scope photographs were taken to preserve the record of this strange phenomenon. At national and international scientific meetings, the pictures were displayed and discussed. The more enterprising of the radar meteorologists created hypotheses to explain what was observed, but no idiosyncracy of atmospheric behavior would satisfactorily account for the observed facts. Other scientists searched for some man-made cause. Perhaps it was an industrial effect, they suggested—traffic and all that. However, in the vicinity of the circle, there was no industrial area with its attendant morning and afternoon gathering and dispersal of automobiles in a parking lot. Moreover, there was no variation between weekday, week end, and holiday echoes in the photographs, as there would have been if any human activity had been the cause. At the center of the circle, as a matter of fact, was nothing but a swamp. And there was the answer.

The swamp was inhabited by red-winged blackbirds which had long since denuded the immediate surroundings of appropriate blackbird food. Each morning the blackbirds left their roosts, radiating outward in search of food. Each afternoon, they returned to their swamp home to spend the night.

Their foraging knew no five-day week nor holidays. A single bird is, of course, invisible to radar, but red-winged blackbirds, insects, or any other substance can give radar echoes if present in sufficient quantity. In the same way, raindrops and sometimes even cloud droplets can be seen on radar.

In the early part of the war, we were just discovering this. What was an airplane spotter's nightmare became the weatherman's golden dream of the proverbial treasure at the end of the rainbow.

For years, meteorologists had talked about cold fronts, picturing them on weather maps with blue lines or by drawing sharp barbs shoulder to shoulder in ink for a black-and-white presentation. The trick was to draw them in the correct

Cold Front on a Radarscope

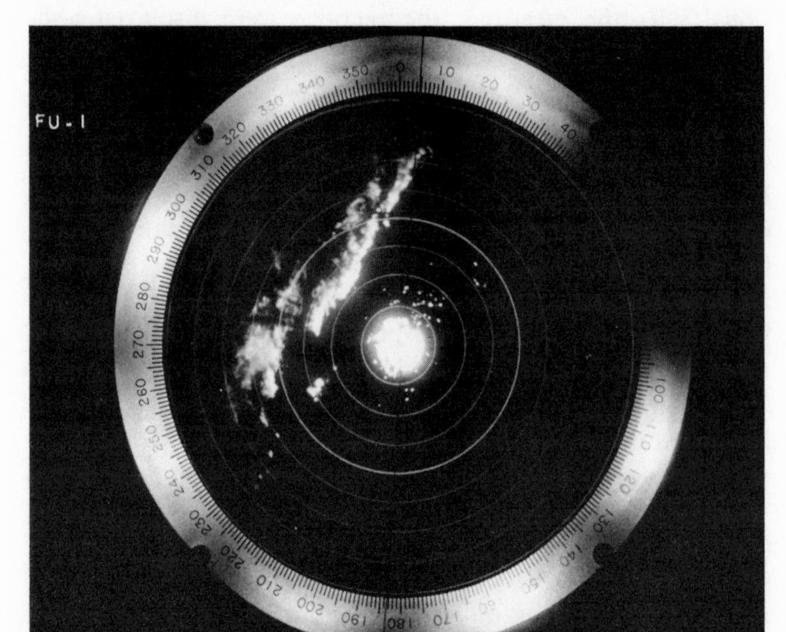

geographical position. At a cold front, the wind changes direction, the pressure is at a minimum, the temperature and humidity alter radically. Literally thousands of cities, towns, and villages each hour report pressure, temperatures, humidity, cloud cover, wind speed and direction, and everywhere meteorologists analyze the reports, saying to themselves, "Cleveland now has a northwest wind, while an hour ago its wind was southwest. The temperature is dropping and the pressure is going up. Akron, on the other hand, still has southwesterly winds, a steady temperature, and a dropping pressure. The cold front must have passed Cleveland, but it has not yet reached Akron." So they put a small blue dash on the weather map between Cleveland and Akron. They then examine reports from other localities, deciding whether the front has or has not passed each one until a series of blue dashes can be made into a continuous line representing the current position of the cold front.

With radar, the cold front appeared as though by magic, clearly drawn on the radarscope. It seemed no trick to translate the line of clouds from the scope to a weather map. The warm front, with its vast areas of bad weather extending into the colder air mass, seemed equally simple to portray, and the isolated thunderstorm easier yet. Of course, the fronts had to be within radar's range—a matter of a hundred miles perhaps. With a sufficient number of radar installations and good communications, it seemed possible to solve the problem of drawing an accurate weather map.

The pot of gold at the rainbow's end was not found that easily, however. Indeed, it has not been quite uncovered yet. With more and more documented cases of frontal movements seen simultaneously in the atmosphere and on the radarscope, it soon became apparent that while the actual front was in some way associated with the line of clouds seen on radar, the position of the two did not necessarily coincide. Nor was radar information the whole answer to the weatherman's prayer. What was seen on a radarscope was too difficult to translate succinctly into words or codes for relaying to other weather stations. Communication time was not available for the interchange of the necessary detailed messages.

For the entire period of about twenty years that I worked for the Naval Weather Service, some part of my effort and energy was devoted to the struggle with the radar-communication problem in concert with my opposite numbers in the Army, Air Force, and Weather Bureau. There is now considerable relaying of radar information around the country, but the problem is not entirely licked by any means.

Tremendous advances have been made in radar meteorology, however, and special weather radars have been designed to perform unique feats valuable to those concerned with weather. Some of these special-duty radars and the reasons for their development are of more than passing interest. Let us consider the "iso-echo contour radar display," for example. You could find these on many commercial aircraft. The pilots quickly realized that radar could help them pick their way through areas of bad weather. Thunderstorms provide turbulent and hazardous flying conditions, of course, and only the inexperienced flyer is not afraid to penetrate into the center of an active storm. Sometimes a whole line of thunderstorms stretches as a boiling, flaming wall across the flight path. A single storm can be skirted, but a line of them must be penetrated. Visually, the individual pickets of the atmospheric electric fence may be all but obscured by the apparent merging and overlapping of the clouds of the separate storm cells. But in the same way that a mountain range has plateaus and passes between the towering peaks, a line of thunderstorms also has soft spots that can be traversed with minor inconvenience and no hazard.

Since many radars can see only raindrops and not cloud

droplets, a radar designed for aircraft use seemed to be just what was needed to meet the pilot's requirements. The active parts of the thunderstorms would be painted on the scope and the innocuous parts would not appear. As long as the pilot avoided flying into an echo, he would be all right. Yet it did not always work out that way. Occasionally, by flying through one of the "passes" between two adjacent thunderstorms, he would get into real trouble.

Why? Research conducted cooperatively by radar meteorologists and commercial airline companies soon provided at least part of the answer. The roughest part of a thunderstorm as far as aircraft passage is concerned is not necessarily the region where the weather is worst—the torrential rain that shows up on radar—but seems to be in the regions where there is the greatest change of weather over the shortest distance. It is not the weather itself that matters as much as its gradient. Sometimes, the clear pass between thunderstorms is just a narrow gap between two very active storm cells. In cross section, within a few miles, the weather sequence changes from bad thunderstorm abruptly to clear and back to bad thunderstorm. The clear area between can turn out to be worse for airplane passage than the storm cells themselves.

What was needed, apparently, was not just a radar, but a radar that could map out contours or gradients to show the pilot where the slopes between good and bad weather were most gentle. Gentle slopes meant easy passage; a tight gradient meant possible trouble.

So radar was asked to discriminate. When the tiny bundle of energy radiating from the antenna was reflected back, the radar receiver was asked to decide whether it was a strong reflection or a weak one. If weak, the echoed signal was allowed to enter the receiver and was duly mapped in its proper position on the radarscope. If the intensity exceeded the preset amount, however, the receiver refused to accept the

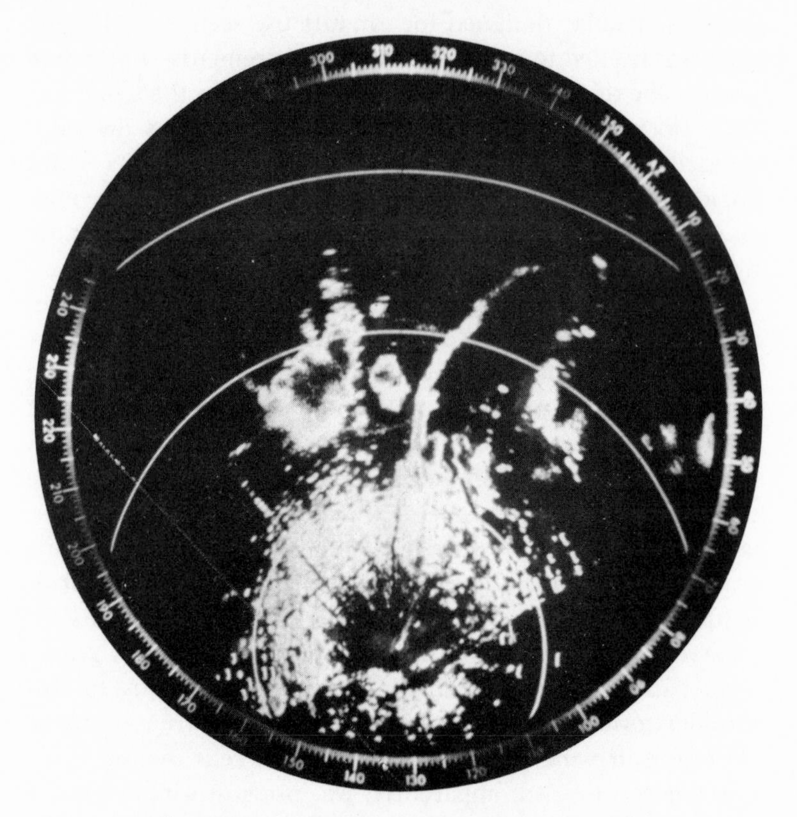

Thunderstorms on an Iso-echo Contour Radar

report and nothing appeared on the scope. A typical thunderstorm echo, then, showed up as a doughnut-shaped spot on the radar screen where the hole of the doughnut was formed by the rejection of the signal from the strongest and wildest part of the storm. Sometimes, the contoured areas appeared in fairly weird shapes, resembling a diamond ring more than a plump doughnut. In the "diamond" part of the ring, the gradients were small and planes were safe, but in the "metal" part, there was a very sharp shift from good weather to poor to bad, and danger threatened a passing aircraft. Much to most meteorologists' surprise, many thunderstorms had two or more active cores or cells, and the echoes did not look as much like a ring as like a piece of Swiss cheese.

Incidentally, a similar electronic principle was used to solve the detection problem of a plane losing itself in a cloud and escaping the searching eye of radar. For this problem, the receiver is asked to judge whether it saw the same echo in the same place the last time it looked. If the answer is yes, the echo is refused. Since the cloud moves very slowly compared to an airplane, it stands still between sweeps, or radar scans, while the plane travels a significant distance. Thus, only the echo from the plane appears on the screen. Of course, this works only when the cloud echo is relatively "soft" compared to that of the airplane. If the cloud echo saturates the receiver, the plane is invisible to the radar as well as to the operator.

One of the most useful radar adaptations for the meteorologist is one in which the antenna does not sweep in circles but just nods its head, looking first overhead and then slowly lowering its gaze until it stares at one spot on the horizon. The structure of a cloud, particularly of a thunderstorm, is obtained in this way. The height of the cloud is determined directly, and since the severity of a thunderstorm—the amount of lightning and hail it contains and the likelihood that it conceals a tornado—varies directly with the height of the storm, the vertical scanning gives much valuable information.

The approximate freezing level in the atmosphere can also be found from this type of radar usage. While knowledge of the altitude at which liquid water changes to ice is useful information, the principal reason for mentioning it here is to give an illustration of how "neat" certain environmental phenomena can be and how thrilling their explanation is to in-

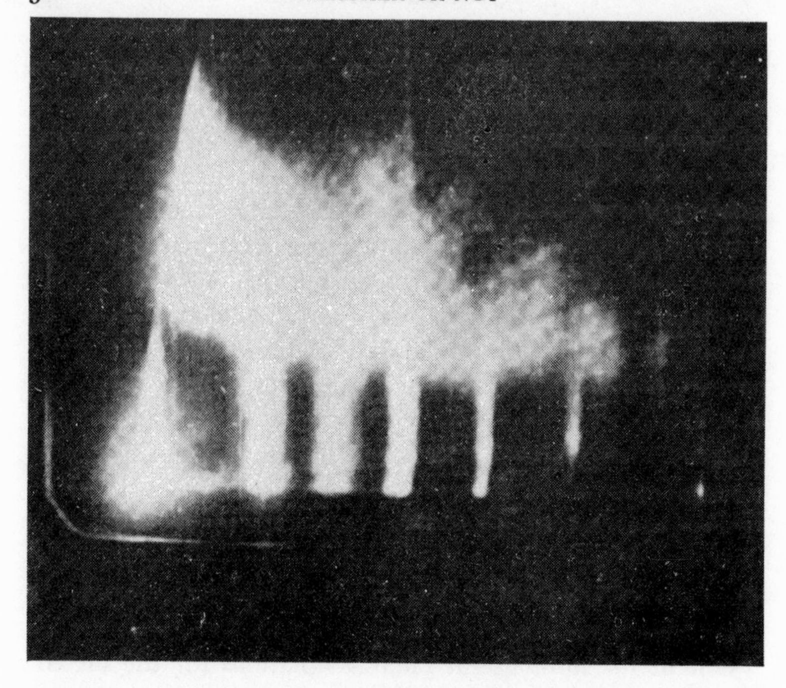

Five Showers Fall from a Large Cloud as Seen on a Vertically Scanning Radar

vestigating scientists.

It was soon noticed that in these vertical cross sections of thunderstorms, the echoes on radar showed a "bright band." Above and below the shallow intense band of echo, the remainder of the thunderstorm was delineated by vertical grey streaks. It was no great trick to find out that the temperature of the atmosphere in the neighborhood of the bright band was always close to 32°F or the freezing level of water. But why? Why should the temperature at which water freezes and ice melts show up so distinctly on a radar screen? The answer which the atmospheric physicists developed was composed of two elements: concentration and reflectivity. Snow-

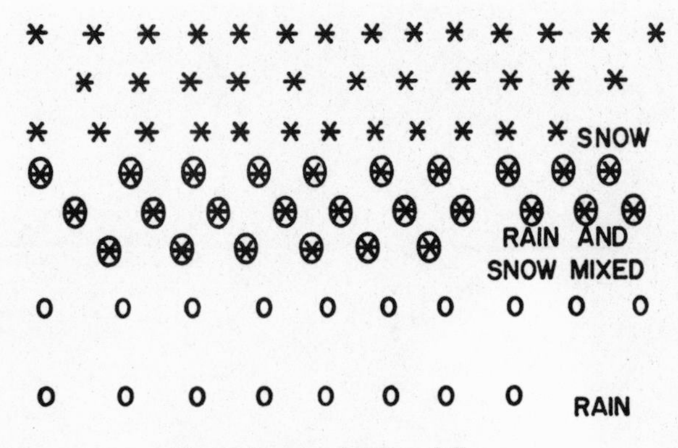

How the Bright Band Forms

flakes fall more slowly than raindrops and reflect radar energy less well. The snowflakes of the upper levels are more concentrated because they fall slowly and remain in the field of the radar beam longer. They would give an intense echo except that their irregular surfaces form very poor mirrors. Raindrops, with their relatively fine mirror surfaces, are too far separated, because they fall fast, to give the type of reflection that results in a bright echo. But at the melting level! At the melting level, the outer surface of the snowflake turns to water and forms a nice mirror. The interior is still essentially a snowflake, however, with its loose, porous structure, so its rate of fall is almost that of pure snow. Many, many good reflectors concentrated in a small section of the atmospheric column show the melting level as a bright band on radar. Below this level, the ice structure collapses, and the more dense raindrops separate one from the other in the remainder of their fall.

Many other advanced and specialized adaptations of radar are now being used to perform valuable tricks in weather science, and radar is a very important tool in man's arsenal of weapons used in understanding and surmounting nature.

Bright Band on a Height-Finding Radar

For the over-all "look-see," radar with its maximum range of 200-250 miles has been replaced in importance by the weather satellite. It seems tremendously attractive to put television cameras and radiation detectors in orbit around the earth to keep track of what is happening.

On April 1, 1960, this was accomplished when the *T*elevision and *I*nfra-*R*ed *O*bservation *S*atellite—TIROS I—was born. With a diameter of 42 inches and a height of 19 inches, sides and top covered with solar cells, the TIROS weighed approximately 287 pounds.

Placed in a nearly circular orbit at a mean altitude of some 475 miles, it revolved about the earth 14½ times every 24 hours. In each 100-minute orbit, the satellite took 32 pictures, storing them on magnetic tape until it passed over a readout station on the ground when it transmitted the record of what it had seen and wiped its storage tape clean to receive the next batch of pictures.

A solution to all the weatherman's problems? Not a bit of

it! In general, weather forecasts since April 1960 have not been significantly better than they were before that date even though a series of nine TIROS satellites has been launched since then.

The nature of the TIROS orbit explains part of the difficulty. Since the plane of the orbit is inclined approximately 48° to the equator, the cameras never see regions toward the poles in either hemisphere. Due to the progression of the orbit, the weather satellite sees, at most, 20 per cent of the earth's surface each day. This is, of course, rather poor coverage.

More satellites simultaneously in space and polar orbits can eventually increase the coverage, but there are other difficulties as well. The satellite sees only the tops of clouds, not what is going on under the top layer nor weather not associated with cloud systems.

What it does see is exciting enough, for fronts look like fronts, hurricanes look as we thought hurricanes should appear, in the same way that continents, peninsulas, lakes, bays, and islands look the way we have been taught to visualize them. It is with hurricanes that weather satellites have had the greatest success, perhaps. If a satellite happens to be over the proper area at the proper time, it can and has detected a hurricane as it was being born. It can track the developing giant storm in its travels, and skilled analysts are able to obtain much information about the severity of the hurricane from transmitted photographs.

3

Balloons and Ballunatics

Perhaps I should be drummed out of the profession as a renegade, but satellites as a weather tool seem to me far less exciting than so many of the other devices scientists have developed to probe the atmosphere. To me, the ingenuity, the achievement are to be found in the rocketry and the satellite, not in the weather application. Perhaps this is all too obvious. It will be a marvelous accomplishment when we put a man on the moon, but his observations of weather patterns on earth from that vantage point will be just so much routine.

I find other devices to measure atmospheric factors much more thrilling. Take the balloon, for example, and all that the atmospheric physicist has done with it.

Originally, the balloon was used to find the height of the ceiling—the lower surface of the clouds when they cover 50 per cent or more of the sky. If you inflate a balloon with just enough helium to give it a fixed amount of free lift, it will rise at a predetermined rate when released. To get the required free lift, you fasten a few weights, equal to the lift desired, to the bottom of the balloon and feed helium into it until the balloon just floats without either rising or sinking. The neck of the balloon is tied off, the weights removed, and at the moment the balloon is released, you start a stop watch. At the instant the balloon disappears from view into the clouds, the watch is stopped, and since you know how high a balloon can rise in a given number of seconds, the ceiling is now measured. At night? That is easy too. Just hang a small light on the balloon and watch until the light disappears.

This use of balloons is more historic than current. It has been replaced at most locations by a ceilometer, which measures ceiling height continuously and automatically. The ceilometer is made up of two parts: a searchlight and a photoelectric cell separated by a distance of several hundred feet on the ground. While the photocell stares vertically upward, the searchlight beam scans up and down. The intensity of the light seen by the cell is recorded. At the base of the cloud, the light beam gives a bright reflection. From the distance between the searchlight and the photoelectric cell, and the angle at which the bright spot is found, the height of the base can be computed. To compete with daylight, the searchlight beam is polarized, or pulsed, and the photoelectric cell geared to accept only the "treated" light.

From the use of the balloon for ceiling measurements, finding wind velocity by balloon follows naturally. As the balloon is released, it is subjected to two forces: the vertical, which is determined by the free lift, and an independent horizontal one, which results from the wind blowing on the balloon surface. If the balloon is tracked, the wind can be measured to altitudes higher than man can build towers.

A theodolite is used for tracking. This is just a telescope with crosshairs in the eyepiece and with scales that measure the amount of turning and tilting of the telescope tube as the balloon target is tracked. Once each minute, the crosshairs of the theodolite are centered on the balloon and the angles of elevation (tilt from the horizontal) and azimuth (direction from north) recorded. With the height of the balloon known from the free lift given at inflation, the position of the balloon at the end of each minute can be calculated. The difference in position from minute to minute translates directly into wind speed and direction.

What a frustrating business these so-called pilot balloon soundings turn out to be. The wind can so easily be measured in good weather, but let the wind blow up a storm and the balloon is soon carried beyond the range of the theodolite. Also, one little cloud can hide the balloon from searching eyes, and the wind sounding is finished. You measure the winds aloft when you don't much need them and lose the measurements when they are vital.

Electronics again provides a way out. A radar reflector can be hung from the balloon so that it can be tracked through clouds to much greater distances and with an over-all increase in accuracy.

With our passion for shorthand terms, the *rawin* (*ra*dar *win*d sounding) all but replaced the *pibal* (*pi*lot *bal*loon wind sounding). To these manufactured words, two more must be added: *rasonde* and *rawinsonde*. Both represent further utilization of the balloon. Wind is only one of the many upper atmospheric measurements that the meteorologist needs. He also wants to know the pressure, temperature, and humidity. The device he hangs from the balloon to measure these three elements he calls a radiosonde and the sounding is known as a rasonde. If he measures the wind simultaneously with these other meteorological factors, he is taking a rawinsonde.

Visualize a small rectangular box weighing approximately two to three pounds. About half the volume of the box and more than half the weight is consigned to a low-powered radio transmitter that can give a series of beeps in a high shrill voice, in low booming tones, or anywhere in between. The voice of the radio is controlled by the meteorological instruments that make up the rest of the radiosonde package.

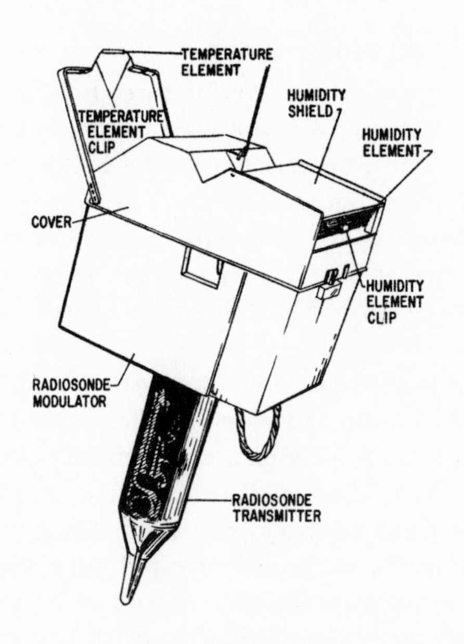

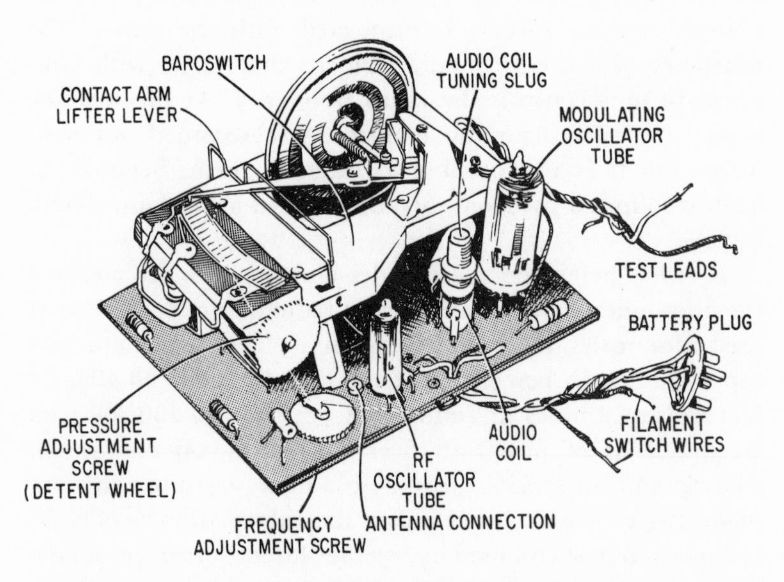

One Type of Radiosonde for Measuring Pressure, Temperature, and Humidity Aloft

A small pressure bellows is the driving force for the entire mechanism. As the balloon rises, the pressure decreases, and the bellows expand. An arm attached to the bellows moves with the expansion traveling across a series of electrical contacts. Since pressure always decreases with height and the balloon always rises until it bursts, to know the pressure it is only necessary to keep count of how many contacts have been made and broken.

In addition to the pressure bellows, there are humidity and temperature circuits in the radiosonde. When the arm attached to the bellows is on a contact, the humidity circuit is connected to the radio. The moisture content of the air through which the balloon passes causes a change in the electric conductivity of a chemically treated strip which is the humidity element of the radiosonde. When the arm moves off the contact, however, the humidity circuit is broken and the temperature circuit is connected with the radio. The resistance of a small ceramic element that varies with temperature now controls the radio frequency. At the weather office, the changing radio emissions are recorded automatically, but it is also possible to listen to them. Beep, beep, beep is followed by boom, boom, boom in a constant, stately fugue.

To what height do radiosondes and rawinsondes measure the atmosphere? If the balloon and radio do not operate to at least nine miles, the sounding is unsatisfactory and must be repeated. A high percentage of the soundings exceed 100,000 feet (some 20 miles up) and a few get close to 150,000 feet. At hundreds of places all over the world, on continents, islands, and on special ships at sea, these measurements are made twice or four times a day, the information pooled by radio or teletype and used by weather forecasters in preparing their upper air weather charts.

As a side note, although it has nothing to do with balloons, rocketsondes should be mentioned here. The height to which a balloon can rise is limited. To reach greater heights, the weather instruments can be packaged into the nose cone of a small rocket. When the rocket is fired and reaches the top of its trajectory, the nose cone is blown off, and a parachute is forced out. The billowing parachute drags out the meteorological instruments, which float back to earth, transmitting weather data as they descend.

I helped coordinate the original Navy rocketsonde for my office, and it seemed to me that the experience I gained as a result of that effort should have been sufficient to qualify me for presiding at one of the Geneva conference tables negotiating some such international problem as disarmament or the Kashmir dispute.

All the components for the rocketsonde were available. A small rocket with a reasonable height potential could be obtained from surplus. As a by-product of advanced radiosonde production, the upper-air measuring instruments and radio transmitter could be obtained without extensive development. Air warfare had long since demanded and obtained parachutes that could meet almost any specification as to load and rate of descent. The catch was the size of the nose cone. Parachute, radio, and instruments all had to be fitted into a very small cylinder at the top of the rocket.

My office dictated the accuracy with which the measurements had to be made. "Can you do this?" I asked the radiosonde manufacturers. "Easily," they answered. "If the rate of fall is no more than so-and-so much, we have no problems." "How about the rate of fall?" "No sweat!" the parachute manufacturers agreed. "How about the size?" And there was the joker. To provide the desired rate of fall, the parachute would just about fill the nose cone, leaving no room for any instrumentation. If a quicker response were demanded of the instruments so that smaller parachutes could be used, the size of instruments grew, more than compensating for the saving in parachute packing space.

In the end, we all compromised, of course, with my office leading the way by lowering the demanded accuracy. But talk about desk thumping with fist or shoe, delegations stalking out in a collective tantrum, desperate telephone calls to various headquarters to find out whether unalterable policies could be altered. . . . We went through the whole bit.

It should be noted that only the instruments on these rocketsondes came down by parachute. The rocket itself just plunged back to earth. This meant, of course, that rocketsondes could be used only over the ocean or over uninhabited land areas. Later, we considered the possibility of a rocket that would destroy itself upon reaching the top of its trajectory so that the equipment could be used around populated regions. We then debated how large a fragment could be allowed to fall freely. To my knowledge no answer was ever found to this question—and no self-destructive rockets ever produced.

But we were considering balloons and not rockets. All the balloons used for pibals, radiosondes, and rawinsondes belong to the same family as the toy multicolored spheres purchased for youngsters at the county fair. They are made of a rubber-like material, filled with lifting gas, and sealed off. When they are released, they go up and up, expanding continually until the balloon material is stretched too thin. Poof! The balloon ruptures, and the flight is over.

There are other types of balloons, however, which work on different principles, and these can do all sorts of tricks beyond going up, exploding, and falling down.

Consider a plastic bag somewhat like the one in which the dry cleaner returns clothing, but one that is essentially spherical—that is, it would be if it were fully inflated.

Every part of the bag is well-sealed, no pinholes or tears,

Inflation of a Constant-Altitude Balloon

except for a narrow neck at the bottom, which is left open. Into this bag, through the open neck, a small amount of lifting gas is fed: either hydrogen or helium. Since the plastic is so thin and light, not much gas has to be added in order to have enough to lift its small weight. As a matter of fact, there is only a small bubble of gas in the topmost part of the plastic balloon, and the rest of the balloon fabric just hangs like a diaphanous veil below the bubble. When the balloon is released, it rises, and the gas trapped at the top expands, gradually untwisting the bottom part of the balloon, forcing out whatever air is contained there through the neck which has not been tied off.

Higher and higher the plastic balloon goes into the air, further inflating itself. At first, it looks like a disembodied spirit drifting skyward, but as it rises, it completely rounds out the fabric creating a sphere. Since the plastic cannot stretch, the balloon can rise no farther. Any more altitude would force some of the lifting gas through the neck, reduc-

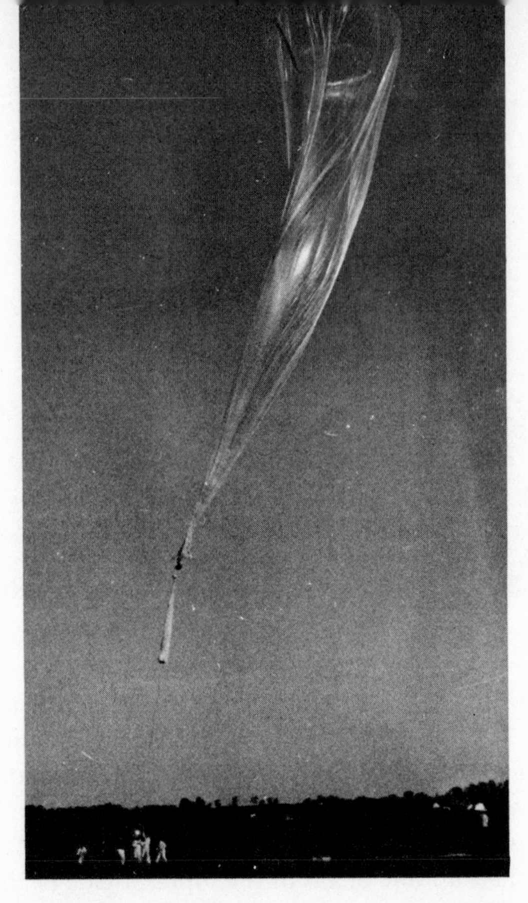

Constant-Altitude Balloon at the Moment of Release

ing the lift and causing the balloon to sink again. So the balloon reaches equilibrium. It gets so high and no higher. It floats. And it can float a long time, several weeks, perhaps, orbiting the earth several times.

How large a balloon are we thinking of? A small one may measure 40 feet in diameter. A large one when fully inflated may reach 150 feet from top to bottom. Even though the polyethylene fabric is considerably thinner than the cellophane wrapper on a cigarette package, the balloon alone may weigh a few thousand pounds. How much of a payload can such a balloon carry? One lifted over six tons in addition to its own weight off the ground.

The facts and figures about these *Skyhooks,* as the balloons are frequently called, are fantastic. The incidents they provoke are equally astonishing. I can remember one day shortly after the balloon had first been developed when a breathless, Huck Finn-type of young man burst into my office. The exuberant quality of his excitement and the myriad of band-aids decorating every exposed portion of his anatomy were immediately apparent.

"I flew one! I flew one!" he announced.

"You flew what?" I asked this unlikely looking and brilliant engineer.

"A *Skyhook.*"

For months, he had been testing the plastic balloons, flying atmospheric instruments suspended from their rigging—and envying the inanimate electronic black boxes their uninhibited rides through the air. The day before his appearance in my office, without telling anyone who might have restrained him, he substituted himself for the equipment scheduled to fly that day. He opened a parachute and fastened the top of it to the balloon, using the normal harness as a less than comfortable seat for his flight.

He fastened a patch to the skin of the balloon so that he could release a little or a lot of gas by pulling a string. That took care of the problem of getting down. Between his legs, he clasped a filled gasoline can so that he could rise by pouring out some gasoline as ballast. Then he took off.

He rose to 5,000 feet and practiced maintaining level flight by releasing the right amounts of gas and ballast. After a brief period of wild oscillation, he mastered the art, and for several hours enjoyed his bird's-eye view of Minnesota and Wisconsin. But then he had had enough. The harness seat was getting more and more uncomfortable, and his slacks and leather jacket were proving quite inadequate protection against the November temperatures. He wanted down and out.

With his newly acquired technique, he released lifting gas gradually, achieving a beautifully smooth glide toward earth. Projecting his glide path forward, he estimated where he would land: right in a maze of power lines.

"Now don't think I panicked or something," my young friend told me. "I knew I had to go up again and make another approach. It just happened that I released ballast by throwing out the gasoline, can and all."

The next approach had to be the final one. Without ballast, he could not go up again. Another gradual descent, but more power lines appeared ahead. His last option had to be exercised: down, but fast. The thump of his ungentle contact with Mother Earth jarred a second string from his hand. This string was designed to draw a sharp knife through the connection between parachute and partially deflated balloon. Still securely attached to both parachute and billowing plastic bag, he was dragged across a field into a barbed-wire fence. There he hung tenaciously until a startled farmer came to release him.

"It was wonderful," he reported. "I'm going to do it again but next time, I'll wear boots. My feet got awfully cold in just loafers."

Indeed, he did fly plastic balloons many times again—sitting in open gondolas and in sealed capsules, flying in clear air and deliberately into thunderstorms to measure atmospheric electricity. After one of the thunderstorm flights, he commented, in passing, about the dilemma of being airsick at an altitude at which one is dependent on a face mask for oxygen. It was his companion on that flight who told me that my friend had almost lost his life on the horns of that dilemma.

In November 1959, this hardy pioneer into space, Charles

B. Moore together with Navy Commander Malcolm D. Ross, flew in a sealed capsule at an altitude of 81,000 feet for over twenty-eight hours making astronomical observations above most of the atmosphere that obstructs observations by astronomers on earth. They took off from Rapid City, South Dakota, and landed near Frankfurt, Kansas. The fragile balloon carried 3,897 pounds of payload—men and equipment.

Those who have anything to do with the flying of plastic balloons live in a world of incredible problems ranging from science fiction to international diplomacy. Take flying saucers, for example. A substantial number of people look skyward and see mysterious objects hovering or darting through the air. As patriotic citizens, or to win their moment in the news, they report what they have seen, and yet another flying-saucer story is extant. When flying-saucer reports are checked, each balloon flight has to be reviewed to see whether a balloon trajectory could possibly have coincided with the sighting. A very substantial number of these UFO's (Unidentified Flying Objects) turn out to be the result of the sun glinting on the gossamer surface of a balloon floating twenty or more miles up in the sky.

While Citizen Skywatcher may be terrified by the prospect of invasion from some extraterrestrial source, his emotional distress can perhaps be ignored. What cannot be passed off quite as easily, is the very real distress of airline pilots sighting a balloon while they are responsible for the safety of plane and passengers, let alone their own lives. Foreign nations also get very upset when their air space is violated by a runaway balloon, and this concern it is not very wise to ignore.

An endless debate rages concerning the hazards balloon flying creates for aircraft, and every effort is made to keep planes and bags separated. Each airfield for miles around is alerted when a balloon is to be released so that no plane will fly in the vicinity for the few minutes necessary for the balloon to reach a safe altitude. All during the time it floats well-above aircraft level it is tracked either visually or by electronic means so that when the time allotted for its flight is over, the area in which it will descend can be warned and air traffic diverted or held during the balloon descent. The balloon always carries a flight-termination device. If it becomes apparent that the flight will drift too close to a population center, the balloon is ordered to destroy itself. The people on the ground are protected from payload impact by the use of a parachute to bring down the payload.

The two principal elements of the debate are the danger of balloons to aircraft, on the one hand, and the valuable information balloons can obtain, on the other. By deliberately banning balloons from airspace used by planes, pilots are deprived of data that could increase the safety of flights. It is a moot question whether the absence of these important data is responsible for more aircraft accidents than would result from balloons and airplanes occupying the same portion of the atmosphere.

For several years, the U. S. Navy obtained vital wind data over the oceans where observations are always few and far between. A daily balloon from Japan would cross the Pacific, the continental United States, and most of the Atlantic. Each two hours, equipment on the balloon would give its electronic signals telling what conditions it was encountering. Radio direction-finding equipment located along coastal regions would spot the balloon and locate its position. Wind speed and direction were obtained from the difference in location from one signal to the next. Always before launching, a wind forecast was made to determine where the balloon was probably going and how long it would take to get there. From this forecast, a timer would be set to explode the balloon before it could get into trouble. If it appeared that it would drift for too long a period of time over the United

States, the timer would go off early while the balloon was still over the Pacific. If, however, it could cross the continent in good time, the explosion was set for descent in the eastern Atlantic before the balloon crossed into Europe.

Elaborate treaties were drawn up with Canada and Mexico, particularly, to cover the contingencies of flight too far north or south. Even so, we had our share of trouble. I remember one indignant call I got from the State Department. Someone occupying the North African desk of that agency gave me a lecture on international good will: the factors generating good relations among the various nations and those that were destructive. Particularly, I was made to listen to the latter. It seemed that I, personally, was responsible for undoing all the good that dedicated work on the part of our Foreign Service personnel and our United States dollars of aid money had accomplished in North Africa.

"What have I done?" I asked at the first opportunity, some five minutes after the phone first rang.

"You've broken our word," came the answer. "How can we teach them to trust us if we break our word?"

It turned out that one of our balloons had gotten away, landing in some desolate stretch of North African desert where, much later, a wandering Arab found it. Eventually, the Arab reached some point of civilization where the tag attached to the equipment could be translated. Still later, the tag was presented to an American consulate. What happened to the tag from that point on, I never found out but "Where were the two dollars the tag promised the finder of the equipment?" my angry caller demanded.

The Strategic Air Command of the U. S. Air Force became angry at us, too. Winds at high altitude can be very strong, and a balloon crossing the Pacific in two days was not uncommon. One such passed close to Alaska going at approximately 240 miles per hour. Not unsurprisingly, it failed to respond to demands that it identify itself. Our ever-alert SAC aircraft scrambled to intercept a possible "hostile." We promised SAC we would let them know the position and course of our balloons in the future.

Those who fly the large plastic bags are not always a nuisance, though. We have helped a great number of government agencies, universities, and scientific institutions with many scientific projects. To get accurate information on the aerodynamic characteristics of a rocket, for example, without introducing the complications of firing and fuel behavior, we picked up a rocket by balloon, carried it to 100,000 feet and dropped it over the instrumented range of White Sands Proving Ground, where each second of its flight downward could be studied. I made the forecast for that exercise, choosing a position in the desert about sixty miles away from the range to allow for the drift of the balloon while it rose to 100,000 feet.

For almost eighteen hours prior to the balloon release that spot in the desert was bulldozed and smoothed until it met the nylon-stocking test: a nylon stocking dragged along the ground anywhere within an acre would survive without being snagged. After all, the balloon fabric is more fragile than a sheer stocking.

The unfueled-missile release also gave us the idea for another experiment. Over a glass of beer one night, we speculated on the flight of a missile fired from a balloon. The following summer, we arranged such a firing using a ship in the Arctic Ocean as base. A rocket that normally reached a peak altitude of 60,000 feet was launched from a balloon floating at 50,000 feet. Since it did not have to push through the dense atmosphere near the earth's surface, it reached an altitude in excess of 200,000 feet.

So much for balloons. One can readily understand why those involved in their flight are called ballunatics.

4

Atmospheric Explosions

Those who design instruments live almost in a world apart. These ingenious men know, in theory at least, of what goes on outside their laboratories filled with oscilloscopes, pressure and temperature chambers, and elaborate timing mechanisms. After all, they say, our instruments make the measurements needed to describe your atmosphere quantitatively. But with these specialists, it is often the story of not seeing the forest for the trees or of knowing more and more about less and less until you know everything about nothing.

Physicist, mathematician, computer programmer, communicator, those involved with weather in any capacity are ultimately concerned with the study of the giant tides, eddies, and whirlpools of the atmosphere. Only by observation, measurement, analysis, and synthesis can they hope to understand what is happening, how it happens, and why it happens. Only with that knowledge can there be any expectation that eventually man will be able to predict weather and ultimately, perhaps, control its course.

First and foremost of our concerns must be those atmospheric events that bring such havoc to the human race—the great atmospheric explosions such as tornadoes and hurricanes. Which of these monsters, the one that comes by land or the creature of the sea, represents nature at its worst? When one thinks of the classic irresistible force for which there is no satisfactory immovable object, the tornado with its winds in excess of four, or five, or six hundred miles per hour probably wins first honors. What can be built to withstand such fury? Like the wanton finger of an exploring urchin poking into colonies of ants, destroying this anthill, crushing those ants, tossing a twig across that tiny highway connecting the colony to its aphid dairy, the tornado dips out of the sky picking up houses, barns, livestock, and automobiles at random, uprooting giant trees as easily as saplings, and strewing them haphazardly over the countryside, smashing, maiming, killing men, women, and children directly with its own force or, more often, indirectly by hurling its debris upon them. Since the year 1900, over 12,000 tornadoes have been recorded in the United States alone, and these have been responsible for some 10,000 deaths. The property damage is assessed in terms of hundreds of millions of dollars.

The tornado is a concentrated cone of fury, averaging only 400 yards in width and bouncing along the ground for no more than some 16 miles, touching down here and there during its half-hour life. In terms of physical extremes, hurricanes and typhoons are mild by comparison: the hurricane's 120–150 mile per hour winds are gentle compared to the 400–600 mile winds of the tornado. Just the vacuum produced in the center of the tornado is dangerous. Examination of the debris after the passage of the funnel storm shows that many of the houses are destroyed by explosion into the intense low-pressure core rather than by the blast of the wind. No such drastic results are produced by the low-pressure centers of hurricanes, which have passed over millions of survivors who described them merely as areas where the air felt oppressive. Statistic by statistic, as long as they refer to the force of the atmosphere, the hurricane is no match for the tornado. It is outclassed in much the same way that a sledge hammer cannot equal the intensity or the speed of a rifle bullet.

Human statistics give a different picture, however. The hurricane dead outnumber the tornado dead even in the United States where hurricane tracking, with its elaborate warning system, has become a fine art. Throughout the world more than 40,000 lives have been lost in hurricanes and typhoons since 1900, and hurricane damage must be expressed not in terms of millions of dollars, as with the tornado, but in billions. If a tornado can be equated to the energy and destructiveness of an atomic bomb, it would take the combined energy of thirteen hundred such bombs to equal the fury of a good-sized hurricane.

Though millions of people have lived through hurricanes and atmospheric scientists have made these giant tropical storms the subject of intensive study, little is yet known of their nature and cause. Even the origin of the name is in doubt.

The direct ancestor of our word, "hurricane," is the Spanish *huracan,* but this word is thought to have an older, Indian, origin. You may take your choice among the Mayan name for the storm god, *Hunraken,* the Galibian tribe's word for devil, *hyoracan,* or the Quiche god of thunder and lightning *Hurakan.* Other similar names originating in the Caribbean include *urican, aracan,* and *huiravucan.* How all these words are interrelated is not known. In the Pacific, a different set of names is given to the same type of storm: typhoon and willy-willy, among others. Regardless of title, this huge storm deservedly strikes terror in the hearts of all who may tangle with it.

Before much more can be said about hurricanes, another set of words must be discussed—not names of old gods or Indian words but scientific terms with very precise meaning.

Sports writers may find twenty different and colorful terms to describe the baseball activities on a busy Sunday afternoon, using such words as blitzed, bombed, edged, walloped, nipped, or topped to report that ten major-league clubs defeated ten others for baseball honors. Other newsmen reporting struggles in a different arena, relating the details of the birth, life, and death of a storm originating in the tropics and threatening the lives and well-being of millions of people, must confine themselves to using the same phrases over and over again or be guilty of scientific lèse majesté.

"Cyclone" is a general term in scientific usage designating any type of rotary motion. Both hurricanes and tornadoes are cyclones. So are the nor'easter of the New England states and the passing low-pressure centers traveling through the midwest. The undisturbed vortex formed by bath water emptying down the drain is a cyclone according to this definition. All that is required is that the rotation be counterclockwise in the northern hemisphere and clockwise in the southern. Such a circulation is called cyclonic, and the accompanying weather is termed a cyclone. Although midwesterners may occasionally take shelter in cyclone cellars, despite their colloquialism, they are shielding themselves from only one very virulent form of cyclone, which is properly called a tornado.

On the other end of the cyclone scale, a slight rotary circulation without strong winds or much decrease in pressure, originating near the equator, is known as a tropical disturbance. The disturbance grows into a depression as the wind increases, but should the winds exceed 38 miles per hour it becomes a tropical storm. Tropical storms with winds between 38 and 75 miles per hour are dignified by being named individually with girls' names in alphabetical order starting afresh each first of January. If the winds in a tropical storm exceed 74 miles per hour (that is, reach hurricane force), a hurricane is formed, and the tropical storm Dolly, Frieda,

WIND SCALE

Descriptive Term	*Miles per Hour*	*Knots*	*Indications*
Calm	Less than 1	<1	Smoke rises vertically.
Light air	1–3	1–3	Direction of wind shown by smoke drift but not by wind vane.
Light breeze	4–7	4–6	Wind felt on faces; leaves rustle.
Gentle breeze	8–12	7–10	Leaves and small twigs in constant motion; wind extends light flag.
Moderate breeze	13–18	11–16	Raises dust and loose vapor; small branches are moved.
Fresh breeze	19–24	17–21	Small trees in leaf begin to sway; crested wavelets form on inland water.
Strong breeze	25–31	22–27	Large branches in motion; telegraph wires whistle.
Near gale	32–38	28–33	Whole trees in motion; inconvenience felt in walking against wind.
Gale	39–46	34–40	Breaks twigs off trees; generally impedes progress.
Strong gale	47–54	41–47	Slight structural damage occurs.
Storm	55–63	48–55	Trees are uprooted; considerable structural damage occurs.
Violent storm	64–75	56–63	Widespread damage.
Hurricane	Above 75	>63	Devastation occurs.

or Ida becomes a hurricane of the same name.

There are an untold number of tropical disturbances. It is almost impossible to find a weather map that does not have several somewhere in the equatorial latitudes. Perhaps fifty of these develop into tropical storms (the exact number is not

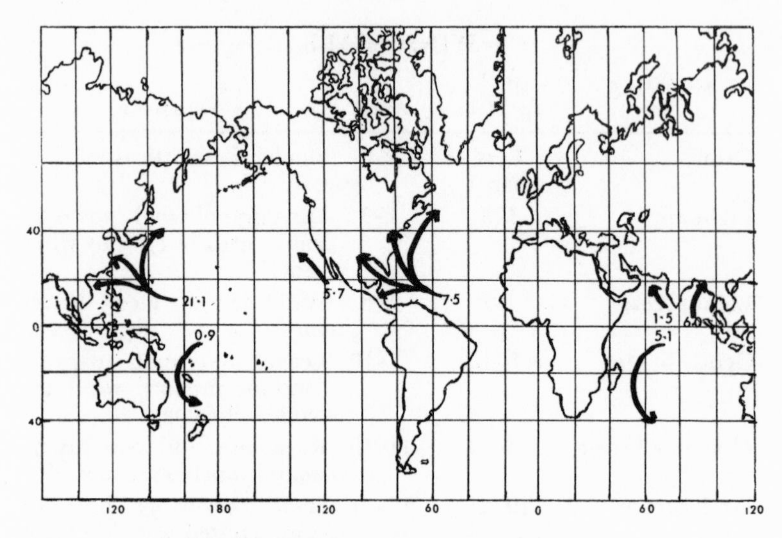

Annual Frequency of Tropical Storms

known because many in the South Indian Ocean and in various regions of the South Pacific are never reported); and of the fifty, only about a third grow to hurricane or typhoon dimension.

The fully developed hurricane! For a distance of two hundred miles in all directions from its center or eye, the winds blow everywhere with at least gale force, exceeding 40 miles per hour, and the water pours from the sky. An inch of water may splash to earth within ten minutes and as much as 30, 40 or 90 inches may be collected at one location during the life of a single storm. Exact records are difficult to obtain, since ordinary methods of collecting and measuring rainfall are poor when the wind drives the water before it with hurricane force.

Within the 400-mile disk that is the whole storm, is an inner circle which may have a diameter of 100 miles in which true hurricane winds blow. Nowhere within this area are the winds less than 75 miles per hour, and often they howl at speeds well in excess of 100 miles. Before the wind carried away the measuring equipment, values of 140 and 150 miles per hour have been recorded, and engineering studies of buildings smashed by hurricane winds show that peak gusts much greater than these values must have occurred to produce the damage observed.

Moving ever closer toward the center of the atmospheric whirling dervish, the winds get stronger and stronger, the clouds thicker and thicker, and the rain heavier and heavier. Then the center is reached. Suddenly everything stops. There is the eye—almost a calm; not only is there no rain, but the sun may be shining. For a distance of 25 to 50 miles, it is difficult to believe that you are surrounded by a storm raging

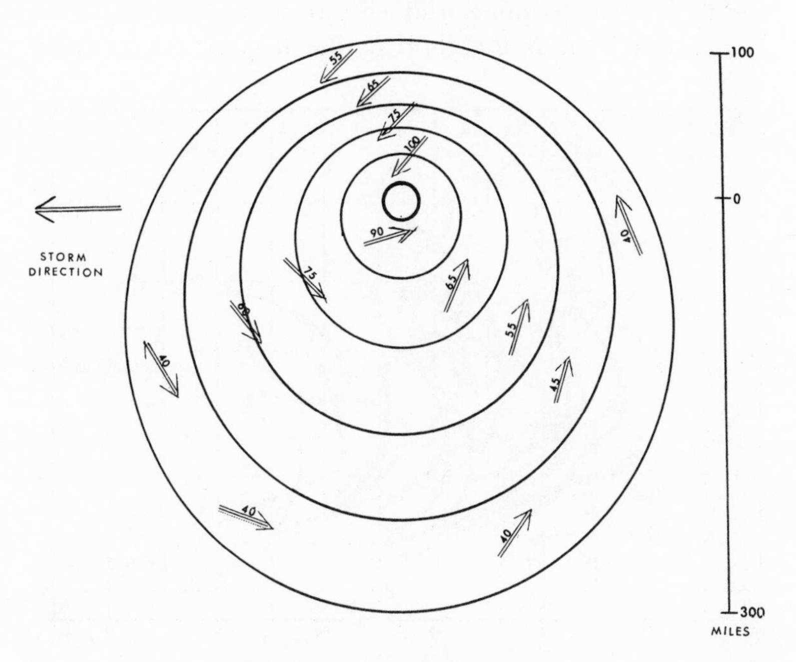

Winds about a Hurricane

with the energy of thirteen hundred atomic bombs of the Nagasaki size. But as time passes, so does the eye and the howling fury begins again.

An encyclopedia of facts and figures about hurricanes and typhoons can be amassed showing extremes of weather that are all but unbelievable, for no two storms are alike. The 96.5 inches of rain collected at Silver Hill, Jamaica, in four days in November 1909 can be countered with the 0.35 inches that fell at Dinner Key in Florida in October 1941—less than a half inch of rain although the winds at Dinner Key reached 123 miles per hour. The paths of the storms cross and recross, circling, touching land here or there, bouncing, or penetrating. They may move east or west, curve and recurve, or not move at all, seeming to poise, gathering strength for a new assault in an as yet undetermined direction.

The hurricane is the child of the tropical sea, growing

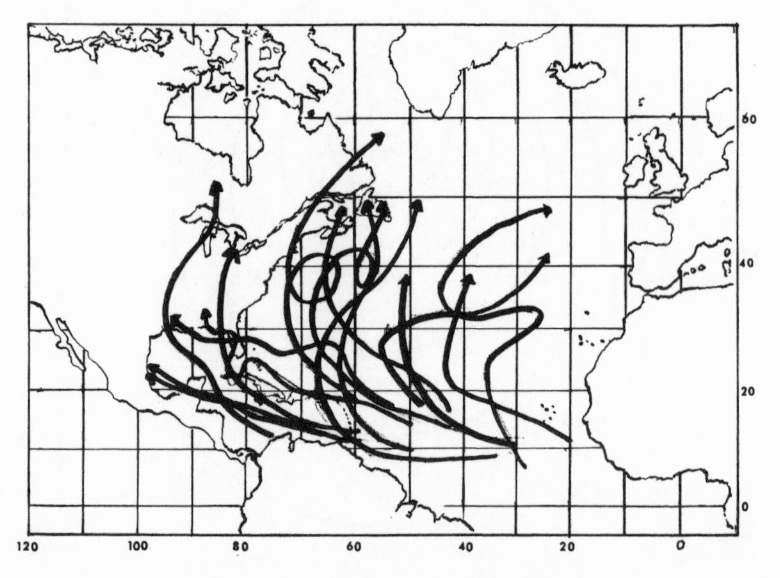

Paths of Some September Hurricanes

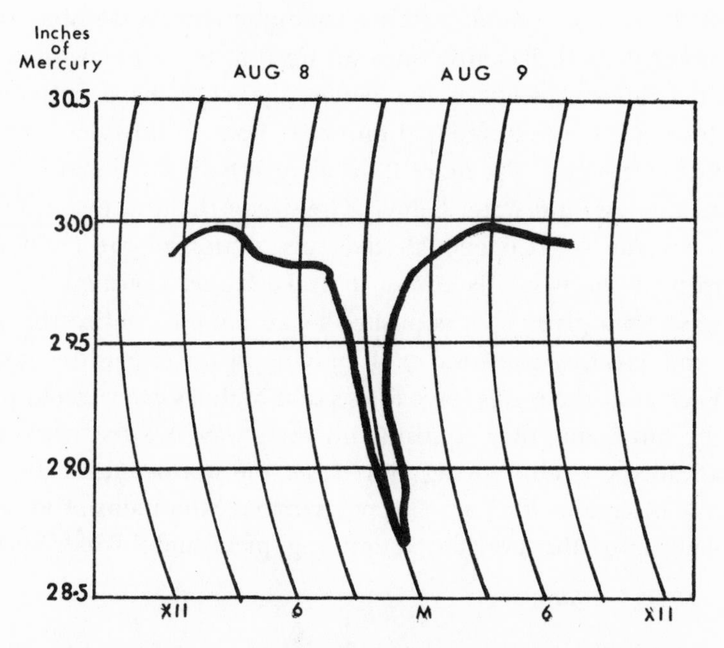

Atmospheric Pressure Changes as a Hurricane Passes Martinique, August 8-9, 1903

stronger as long as it maintains contact with its parent and dying for want of nourishment when it passes over land or into inhospitable northern waters. The sea, too, provides it with its most deadly weapon. Neither lowered pressure nor tempestuous wind causes widespread damage. Life and property are primarily lost in the sea, which invades the coasts and destroys by inundation. Death by drowning is the most common hurricane fatality.

The storm must be visualized as a whole to understand why the bowl of the ocean can no longer contain its salty liquid and sends it surging inland. The driving mechanism of the great circular storm is at the center, where the pumping low pressure produces the whirling of the air at the walls of the eye. The fluid, rotating atmospheric mass transfers its momentum inefficiently outward until at the edge, two hundred miles or so from the center, the winds have been reduced from a hundred-odd miles per hour to thirty or forty. But everywhere the more fluid air exerts its frictional force on the less fluid water below. The size of the disk that is the hurricane is great enough that any section of the circular path of the winds is almost a straight line. Constantly the water in a given area is pushed by an almost unidirectional wind, creating giant waves all moving in the same direction. Even after the waves leave the section of the ocean covered by the hurricane, they continue on their way as a tremendous advancing swell, moving away from the storm until a shore line interrupts their smooth progression. Mountains of water pour onto the beaches, crumbling piers and breakwaters,

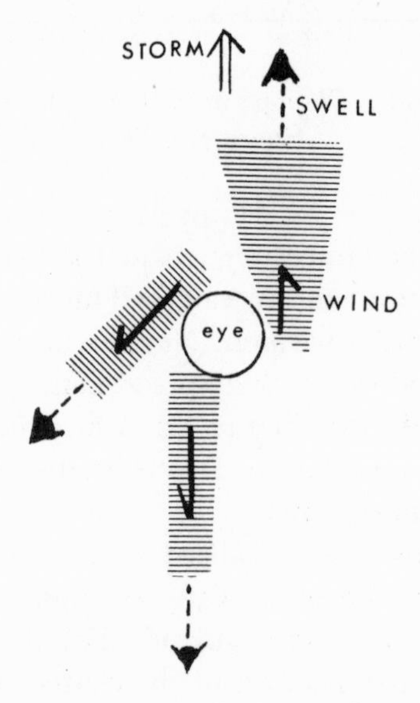

Swell Leaves the Storm Area

tossing moored ships into the main streets, and washing away houses.

A foolhardy few, abandoning shelter to see what is going on or to secure a flapping shutter, may be killed by the direct action of the wind as they lose their footing or are struck by a dislodged tree limb, but all who have not taken to high ground can lose their lives from the storm's watery surge no matter where they are hidden.

It is the growing swell that warns the Caribbean or the Melanesian native of the coming storm. On a day unusual only because the trade winds blow more lightly and the customary daily shower does not occur, a long, low swell is noticed rolling in from the southeast. No visible wind accounts for the orderly progression of the mounding water. It is a signal, not to be acted upon, but to be watched for further developments.

The following day, the swells are longer and higher. They can be seen breaking on the beaches and heard crashing as far inland as a half a mile. Except for the absence of the trade wind, the weather is not yet threatening, but as the high, thin cirrus clouds move in like mares' tails, growing to form a milky layer high in the sky, the weather-wise native has received his hurricane or typhoon warning. He pulls his fishing boat high on the beach and spends the hours during which the wind builds up in erratic gusts putting up shutters, nailing down neglected shingles, and checking on the supply of kerosene and food. Meanwhile, his wife is gathering mops and rags, which she knows will be needed when the enveloping rain begins. At the height of the storm, there will be no apparent difference between air and water. It will be as though the house were picked up and submerged in the ocean with water forcing itself in through every crack and crevice. Only a submarine or a sealed space capsule could remain internally dry against such an onslaught.

The native has seen the sign given by the sea and needs no flying hurricane flags or radio advisory to tell him to take heed. According to some men who served the Navy at Fleet Weather Central Guam in the Pacific, the natives studying the subtle signs often did better than the university-trained weather forecasters who studied their instruments and filled the ether with massive broadcasts of atmospheric data. Once, twice, the Americans would call a typhoon alert and proceed to take their carefully considered precautions. The Guamanian continued to live his regular life ignoring the dire warnings issuing from the military. Typhoons would develop but somehow miss Guam. Then, another storm might threaten, and even before the hurricane flags were pulled up to flagpole tops, the natives of Guam would be scurrying about to protect themselves and their possessions. That time the full fury of the storm would strike the tiny atoll.

I cannot guarantee the validity of this observation. Somewhere, once, I heard the story of the Arizona Indian whose weather forecast was deemed infallible but who explained one day that he could not give the prediction at that time because a tube in his radio had burned out and he had missed the weather broadcast from Los Angeles. I have been a doubter about native prescience ever since.

But the scientist, too, has been much intrigued by the motion of the ocean resulting from the action of a hurricane, and for many years, intensive research was conducted to see whether it was possible to detect and track these storms from remote locations by use of the water action. A Jesuit priest, Father J. B. Macelwane, working in St. Louis, Missouri, noted along with others that a very sensitive seismograph on occasion traced a distinctive pattern showing a rhythmic and prolonged disturbance of the earth's crust. Completely unlike the recording of an earthquake, the tiny jitterings of the seismograph seemed to occur only when a tropical storm prevailed in the Atlantic or Caribbean. Guessing that these microseisms originated at the storm, Father Macelwane tried to use them to locate the disturbance. Near St. Louis, he set up three microseismographs (seismographs especially sensitive in the range of these small crust disturbances) in a triangular array.

"If a wave in the earth's crust were to pass the forward seismograph first and then affect the other two seismographs simultaneously," Father Macelwane reasoned, "I would know that the wave came from a point at right angles to the two seismographs. If the disturbance comes from some other direction, I can compute where it comes from by timing when it passes each of the three seismographs."

In the middle of the plain states, the tripartite seismometers were set up, and, indeed, whenever the characteristic microseismic pattern became apparent, a hurricane was raging in the Atlantic. Moreover, the direction indicated by Father Macelwane's computations seemed to point directly to the storm.

Detecting a hurricane at a distance of more than fifteen hundred miles was quite a feat, obviously. The hopes of some of the meteorological community soared at the prospect of finding a method that would provide for early detection of these storms and possible tracking from a considerable distance. Not everyone was quite as impressed, however. While some believed that the seismographic array picked up the disturbance of the earth's crust produced in the eye of the hurricane, others asserted that the vibrations carried through the land mass stemmed from the pounding of the swell on the coast or on the continental shelf. Early detection was impossible, they felt, because the tremendous swell was produced only after the storm was mature. Tracking was equally impossible because the swell that reached the coast might have been generated several days earlier and would only indicate where the storm had been, not where it currently was or where it was going.

At their meetings and in their journals the fight raged on, with some scientists on both sides adhering adamantly to their respective positions while others vacillated, changing from storm to surf theories and back at frequent intervals as new evidence supporting one view or the other was presented.

As time went on, two further facts developed. Tripartite microseismic stations located along the Atlantic coast did not give directions pointing to the eye of the hurricane. Thus, the storm origin of the seismic tremors had to be discounted. On the other hand, microseisms were not always observed when the coastal plain was receiving its greatest pounding. The surf theory had to be discounted as well.

My position in all this? I tried to act the part of the great mediator, theorizing that the recorded microseisms might reflect two separate actions at the earth's crust: one developing at the eye of the storm and the other resulting from the storm-generated swell. While tapping a finger of one hand lightly at the center of a desk, I would jar the edge of the desk with the full force of the other hand. "This, gentlemen, is what I think you are observing," I suggested.

To develop my hypothesis, I did research first in Miami, working with the people responsible for the Atlantic microseismic network, and then on Guam in the South Pacific, working with those responsible for the typhoon network. The analysis seemed to bear out my contention, although it was difficult to isolate the frequency of the light tap from the noisy oscillations produced by the jarring. In due course, I presented my results to the scientific community.

It was just about that time, however, that a young Englishman performed a mathematical exercise saying, in effect, "A plague on both your houses." Longuet-Higgins showed mathematically that no simple disturbance at the surface of the ocean, whether at the eye of the storm or along the surf line, could be transmitted to the ocean bottom. Only if two waves interacted at just the correct angles could the effect pass through the water to the bottom without attenuation, there to be relayed through the crust of the earth to appropriate measuring equipment. The standing waves, his theory demanded, might be generated in the tail of a hurricane where swell from two different parts of the storm could intersect or they might come from certain combinations of coastal geography and thudding surf where the oncoming water was reflected at just the right angles.

My work suffered the fate of so many good but uninspired research efforts that are meaningful and worthwhile until another scientific break-through renders them antiquated and worthless almost overnight. What remains most vividly with me as a result of this work has nothing to do with atmospheric behavior. In Miami, I obtained firsthand experience with escalating hotel prices as winter months succeeded those of fall during my stay there; and in the Pacific, on my way to Guam, I was accorded the doubtful privilege of seeing absolute disgust expressed on over five hundred male faces simultaneously.

I had managed to hitch a ride on a "congressional" plane between Hawaii and Guam. The Navy transport was proceeding empty to Japan, there to pick up traveling congressmen for their return trip stateside. At four in the morning, the plane with me as the only passenger arrived at Johnston Island for refuelling. Navy communications had been just so efficient and no more. Johnston Island had been alerted to the plane's arrival, but no one had thought to pass on the information that the congressmen were not aboard. When I stepped from the plane's cabin, I was momentarily confronted by the commanding officer, the executive officer, and all the military personnel of the island in dress whites, standing in parade formation complete with band. The tableau dissolved instantaneously as the true facts of the passenger manifest became apparent, and I was left in the sudden predawn darkness with nothing but hundreds of disgusted visages firmly etched on my retinas. Except for a few published papers in which no one is interested any longer, these memories are the sole survivors of my microseismic experience.

Longuet-Higgins effectively dissipated the scientists' dreams of detecting and tracking hurricanes easily, comfortably, and safely from a distant location by using microseismic techniques, and exclusive rights to sea conditions as a forecasting aid were returned to the Caribs and Melanesians. But early warning, tracking, and forecasting of the tropical giants which drunkenly wend their way to island and continental shores remain as imperatives to the weather services of the United States. Safety of people and property can be attained only if there is timely preparation. If these tasks cannot be performed at a distance and easily, they have to be done the hard, and perhaps dangerous, way.

To be quite certain where a hurricane or typhoon is at any given moment, there is nothing more effective than being within the eye of the storm. The United States Navy and Air Force have been tracking storms in this direct manner since World War II. The unbelievable nature of these repeated feats of heroism can only be guessed at by those who fly air lines always intent on maneuvering to escape bad weather.

The hurricane-hunters, basically identical with commercial aircraft, but fitted with radars and atmospheric measuring equipment instead of passenger seats and cargo space, approach the hurricane at an altitude of less than a thousand feet, circling with the wind from one massive rain squall to another, always edging closer and closer to the center, riding the wind from a relatively tame 50 miles per hour to velocities in excess of 100 miles per hour. No horizon guides them as air and water blend into a single liquid medium that somehow they must penetrate. Nor does the wind blow steadily. A wind reported as 100 miles per hour is only 100 on the average. The harder it blows, the greater are the variations in its speed. In seconds, it changes from 75 to 130 and back again. Nor is the gustiness only in a horizontal plane. Each change in wind speed is part of a three-dimensional eddy, so that the aircraft hurricane hunter rides a roller coaster through the storm with incredible sweeps. The almost solid air lifts it at hundreds of feet per second only to pull away its erratic support from under the wings, plunging the plane downward at an even faster rate.

The 27-man crew of the hurricane-hunter seems to find comfort in the knowledge that a downdraft cannot persist all the way to the surface, but even convinced as I am in the immutability of the physical laws, I cannot conceive that they do not anticipate immersion in the watery depths with each downward plunge. With wave heights of fifty or sixty feet below them, it would seem that the ocean stretches up long arms to pull them down to disaster.

How the aircraft structures withstand these extreme buffetings is another source of wonder and amazement. Mostly the vibrating wing tips cannot be seen in the heavy rain, and the roar of the wind and pelleting water effectively drown out the irregular sputtering of the straining engines. Perhaps some comfort is found in not seeing or hearing the protests of the man-made creation that is defying the awesome natural force. At any rate, military crews repeatedly fly these missions and act as though they were just on another routine assignment.

During the flight, when the penetration has been successful, they get their moment of respite in the eye of the storm.

There, in an area of some twenty-five-mile radius, they can relax for a while as they circle in the relatively calm air making their meteorological and oceanographic measurements. Of all the computations performed in the eye of the storm, the most important is the one determining the aircraft's position. When the navigator has fixed his latitude and longitude coordinates, he has also established the location of the storm. A radio fix is relayed to the Hurricane or Typhoon Weather Central, and the correct track of the storm is plotted on the weather map. Appropriate storm advisories are issued to the military services and to the public. Usually, within twelve hours, another aircraft will be sent out to pinpoint the storm again. The earlier plane has completed its mission. After its crew has had its coffee and cigarettes in the undisturbed eye, they have no further function to perform. They must only fight their way through the same elements again in order to return to base.

Unless the tropical storm is below an orbiting satellite or within radar range of a powerful shore radar station, the hurricane-hunters must make their routine flights, checking on each suspicious area in an effort to detect an incipient storm. If the alarm proves not to be false, they must fly into, over, and around each storm throughout its development.

Occasionally, their work is made easier because both the Navy and the Weather Bureau spot floating automatic weather stations in likely ocean areas in an effort to get first word of an impending storm. There are a variety of these devices, but each accomplishes essentially the same mission, measuring air and water temperatures, wind speed and direction, and atmospheric pressure. While the measurements are continuous, once each six hours a mechanism in the buoy says "Now!" Momentarily, all the readings are "frozen" until they are transmitted by radio in a general broadcast to be received by any station within 1,000 miles or more range.

A Hurricane as Seen on Radar

The difference among these floating automatic weather stations is largely one of size and therefore of durability and sophistication. The largest, NOMAD—with pride or shame, I must confess that I am responsible for the acronym: *n*avy *o*ceanographic *m*eteorological *a*utomatic *d*evice—is a twenty-foot boat with a ten-foot beam. It can be anchored in deep water, to depths of over 11,000 feet, using a polypropylene cable, which has the unique characteristic of having almost the same density as water. It is essentially weightless in the

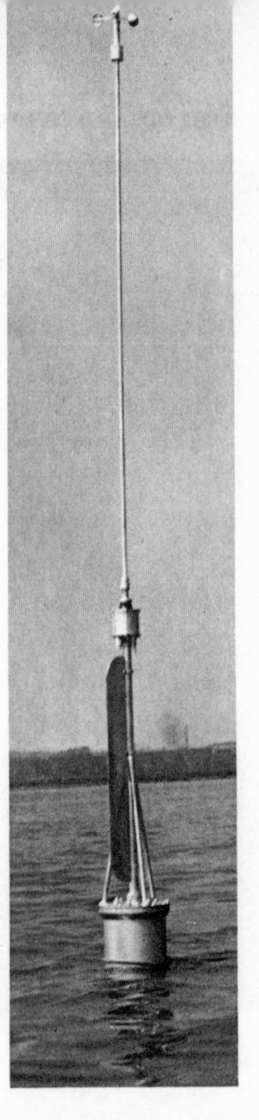

Free-Floating Buoy Automatic Weather Station

water; otherwise the length of anchoring cable would be more than NOMAD could support.

Since NOMAD is anchored, its position is always known, and, with its large battery capacity, it can remain in operation unattended for long periods of time. Indeed, it is now planned to use an atomic power plant aboard so that its life can be extended indefinitely. One fascinating feature of this floating automatic weather station is its sensitivity to wind speed. If the wind picks up and exceeds a certain preset number of miles per hour, the atmospheric measurements are radioed not at six-hour intervals but each hour. The unexpected broadcast constitutes a real hurricane warning.

In addition to NOMAD, there are several free-floating buoys that can be set out in potential hurricane areas and a parachute weather buoy that can be dropped from a plane into waters which should be monitored. These free-floating buoys must be tracked using radio direction-finding methods since the reported data are useless unless the position of the buoy is known.

Unfortunately, it seems impractical to stud enough of the ocean surface with buoys to achieve any reasonable assurance that they will detect an incipient hurricane or typhoon, and usually the buoys cannot survive the impact of a hurricane. As the hurricane closes on it, it is destroyed and its valuable voice is heard no more.

Automatic weather stations were developed during World War II in order to provide coverage at places where it was impossible or undesirable to establish a manned weather station. These were all land stations for erection on islands, atolls, or in the Arctic wastes. It was a noble concept which did not work out very well. Something always went wrong with them. In the Arctic, the wind-measuring equipment would freeze up. In the tropics, the jungle would swallow the instruments in short order. To my knowledge, none ever became fully operational although one achieved a unique status. It became a shrine for the natives of a South Pacific island. An aviator friend of mine reported seeing it in the late fifties, shiny, freshly painted, surrounded by a well-kept garden, and with a pebbled path leading to it. Its last broadcast had been heard in 1945.

5

Is Our Climate Changing?

One of my instructors at M.I.T., whose major interest was the study of hurricanes, told my class that once he had had a passionate desire to experience one at first hand. He was a native of the Boston area, and during his lifetime only one hurricane had ever struck New England, grazing the edge of Cape Cod in 1924. In an effort to increase his chances of seeing one, he decided to go where hurricanes abound. He saved his money, arranged his affairs, and went to spend the hurricane season in Puerto Rico. That was the year 1938, when New England was hard hit by a massive hurricane and Puerto Rico escaped all major storms.

Is our climate changing? During the years since 1900, New England has been battered by only nine fully developed hurricanes, but of this number, five occurred in the last twenty years. Florida, on the other hand, experienced a total of forty-nine full hurricanes during the interval from 1900 through 1963, with the last thirteen years of that period contributing only three. But in 1964 alone, large areas of Florida were devastated by three major hurricanes.

Old-timers tell us what winters were like when they were young in tones which imply that we, as members of a spoiled, younger generation, have deliberately reduced winter's rigors to accommodate our soft and overcivilized ways. But even our teen-agers can be overheard talking about the severe winters they knew when they were young! And, periodically, newspapers carry articles suggesting that atomic bombs have modified our weather conditions.

One answer to the question of whether our climate is changing can only be an emphatic yes. Viewed in terms of billions of years, climate has changed considerably. The average temperature in northern latitudes some forty million years ago was approximately 25° higher than it is today. On the other hand, the climate was significantly colder about twenty thousand years ago.

Who calls "foul" to this answer? The question about changing climate was not raised in terms of geologic ages but with respect to the present and the immediate past. Despite the availability of all the data that could be desired, this question cannot be answered as easily. While some maintain that there is a warming trend and others believe they detect a general cooling, most climatologists, when sufficiently pressed, will say that they do not know. All climatologists of every persuasion agree, however, that whatever change may be taking place, it is much too small to be noted by the physiological capacity of man.

Memory of past weather is tricky, and variations from one year to the next, an apparently random change from colder to warmer or from greater to lesser snowfall, are much greater than any long-range trend. The one or two degrees' change in mean temperature that some claim to have noted during the past fifty or so years would never be noticed by humans pursuing their usual activities of going to work or tending their farms.

Various graphs can be drawn to show the difficulty of detecting a trend against the extreme annual variations. To illustrate, several are reproduced here, showing the mean

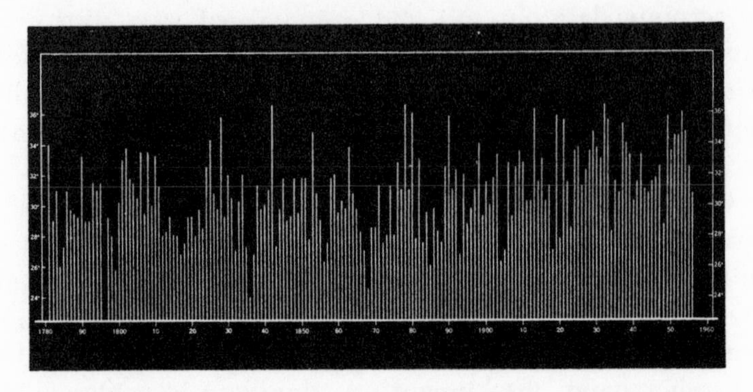

Mean Winter Temperatures at New Haven, Connecticut

winter temperature at New Haven, Connecticut, for the period 1781–1956, the seasonal snowfall for central Maine between 1812 and 1956, and various aspects of the hurricane picture.

What is exceedingly interesting to the atmospheric physicist is the marked increase in the number of typhoons observed in the Pacific Ocean since 1942 as well as the considerable increase in the number of tornadoes over the United States in recent years. The typhoon story is perhaps

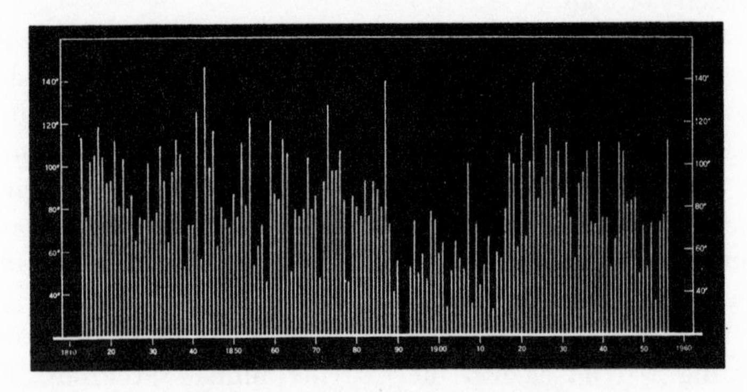

Mean Snowfall in Central Maine

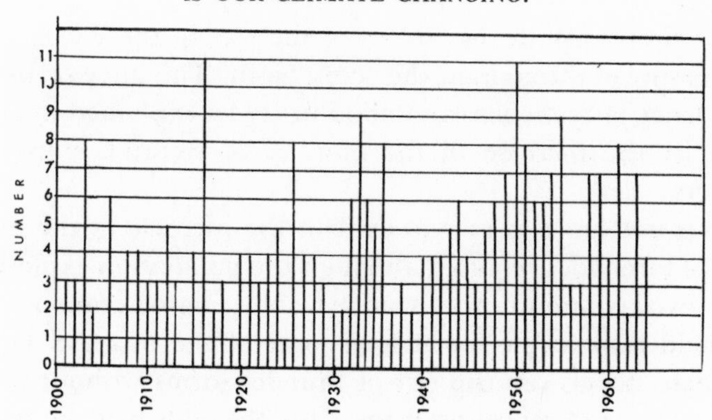

Frequency of Atlantic Hurricanes

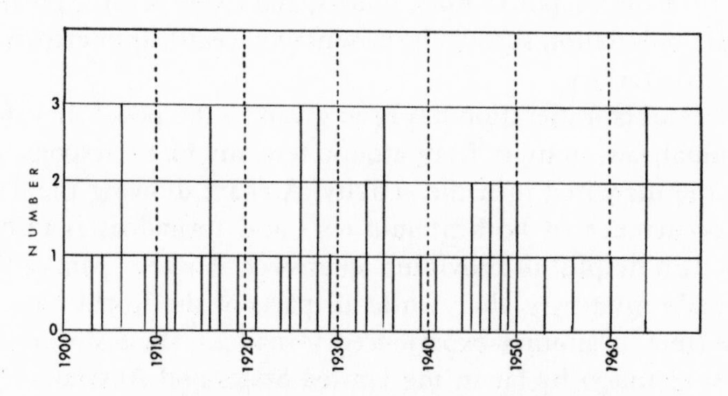

Frequency of Hurricanes Striking Florida

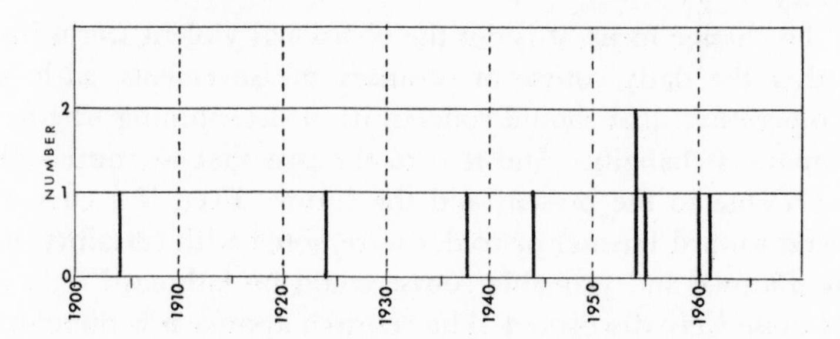

Frequency of Hurricanes Striking New England

quite simple. With the advent of the war in the Pacific, our forces spread throughout the ocean basin. The increase in the incidence of typhoons can undoubtedly be explained in great part by the increase in the number of record-keeping observers.

It is not quite as easy to explain the increase in the number of tornadoes reported although the population explosion, improved communications, and the burgeoning economy can be held responsible for at least some of the increase. Fewer of these storms can dip out of thunderstorms without someone seeing and reporting them. Also, the odds that the whirlwind will cause significant damage to man-made objects, such as automobiles, power lines, houses, and roads become greater as the population spreads its productive wealth into erstwhile virgin territory.

Serious consideration has been given to the possibility that residual radioactivity from atomic tests might be responsible for the increased tornadic activity. A chart showing the date of occurrence of both atomic tests and tornadoes is rather less than helpful in providing an answer. Another part of the tornado mystery is that, while all parts of the world have at one time or another experienced tornadoes, these storms are most common by far in the United States and Australia. No satisfactory explanation for this coincidence has been offered either.

To change focus, it is not the occasional violent storm but rather the daily course of ordinary measurements, such as temperature, that should concern us in determining whether climate is changing. And it is to the past that we must look for a clue to the present and the future. Even if a current trend toward warmer or colder were noted with certainty, its significance and probable course could be fathomed only if its cause were discovered. The research approach is therefore to find temperature maxima and minima in past ages and to link them with what was going on at the time: changes on earth, at the sun, or elsewhere in the solar system. If it could be determined that an increase or decrease in solar activity or carbon dioxide seemed to be responsible, present variations in the sun or of the components of the air could be studied. Then, perhaps, we would know what the future holds for us with respect to weather.

Of course, a reasonable query involves how we know anything about the temperature, thousands, millions, or billions of years ago. Atmospheric scientists are not competent to make this determination but turn to their fellow geophysicists, the geologists and paleontologists, for information, which has been gleaned from the most esoteric clues in a demonstration of detective prowess that makes Sherlock Holmes' deductions appear crude by contrast.

The time periods during which various layers of sedimentary rock were deposited are known with a reasonable degree of certainty. These rocks can then be examined for both animal and vegetable fossils. From the knowledge of the temperature adaptability of the life forms responsible for the fossil residue, the climate prevailing at the time of their deposit can be ascertained. This evidence can be matched with other bits and pieces of evidence such as the ratio of isotopes oxygen-18 to oxygen-16 in certain shellfish fossils since it has been established that this ratio is dependent upon the temperature of the sea-water habitat of the shellfish.

Palms, laurels, magnolias, peppers, acacias are plants of subtropical and warm-temperate climates, but their fossil remains are found in southeastern Alaska, for example, in rocks dating to the Eocene age. Farther north, in the currently barren tundra at the northern tip of Grinnell Land, within 8° of the North Pole, remains of spruce, pine, hazel, birch, poplar, and willow—growths of a colder temperate climate—are found in rocks of the same geologic age. Clearly, the zone we now call temperate prevailed much farther north some tens of millions of years ago.

Whether the plant fossils can be identified with current growths or not, their anatomy gives telltale evidence of the climatic conditions prevailing during their life. Leaves of deciduous trees growing in humid, tropical climates, regardless of family, genus, or species, are predominantly large, thick, undissected, and smooth margined. These leaves may be contrasted with those of a cooler, but still humid, climate, which are generally smaller, thinner, and toothed or lobed.

Various forms of animal fossils substantiate the vegetable evidence. Reef-building corals perform their underwater construction chores only in the warm, clear seas of the tropics and subtropics. When coral reefs are found in northern waters, they confirm that at one time milder temperatures prevailed in the area.

Vertebrates which roamed the earth in past eons contribute their piecemeal stories as well. In the rocks and stones of

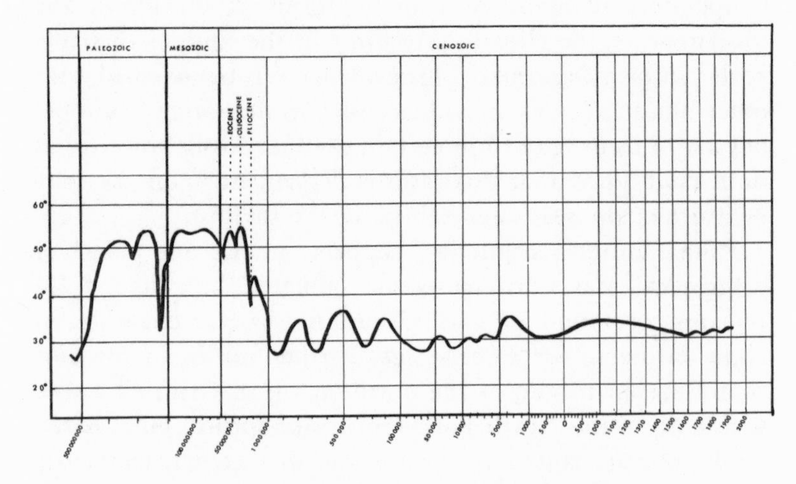

Temperature Changes through the Ages

Wyoming and the Dakotas are found the signatures of alligators, while arctic reindeer and musk oxen once roamed through California, Texas, and Mississippi. Walrus at one time resided in South Carolina and Georgia. In a complete temperature reversal, the alligators invaded the northern reaches during the Eocene and Oligocene epochs while the Arctic stretched southward during the Pleisocene glacial epoch.

Even without fossils, the rocks themselves testify in the "Case of the Changing Climate." Is the sedimentary rock red in color? The erosion of red soils and their subsequent deposition speak of a warm, humid climate. How old is the rock? Aha! We can write down another deduction. Sand dunes and coal deposits, salt, and gypsum beds can also be called to the stand to testify. As final witnesses, the mean heights of continents and relative percentages of land areas versus water areas bespeak of the amount of melting of the polar ice cap and therefore of the prevailing temperature.

The climatic situation today on this geologic scale can be described as being about two-thirds of the way out of a cold glacial period, approaching a warm interglacial era. Well, there is one answer: our climate will be getting warmer for the next several thousand years.

One of three major hypotheses, or a combination of them, is used to account for the significant temperature variations. Obviously, the lack of consensus indicates that no one really has explained why the temperature scale consists of such irregular peaks and valleys.

There are those who believe that changes in the earth's crust are responsible, but even for those holding this over-all point of view, there is no agreement about what changes produced the effects. The north pole may have migrated. A polar shift would account for glaciation in various regions at various times, but unfortunately for this theory, there is evidence that the last major period of glaciation occurred simultaneously over the entire earth. A migratory pole should account for regional changes only.

Some geologists, also proponents of the crustal theory, maintain that mountain building is responsible for the various temperature trends, and, indeed, there is excellent correlation between the general periods of mountain building in the earth's history and subsequent glaciation. Mountains are held responsible by a sort of chain-reaction mechanism. In the first place, mountains, particularly those oriented in an east-west direction, interrupt the interchange of air between equator and poles. This results in colder polar caps and therefore more snow and ice accumulation. Since snow and ice reflect sunlight very efficiently, there is less solar heating of the surface than there would be without the ice cover. The temperature is further reduced. Even if the mountains are not oriented in an east-west direction, the temperature would be lowered because the tops of mountains are colder than the bottoms. Snow and ice collect more readily on the mountain tops, and, again, reflection of the sun's rays magnifies this difference. Unfortunately, for this hypothesis at least, it appears that there has been no growth in mountains during the last twelve million or so years. Yet, since that time, the world has experienced not only several significant temperature changes but has also survived a major ice age.

The efficiency with which solar radiation heats the earth's surface can be modified by other changes in the earth's crust besides mountain building. A volcanic eruption can scatter dust into the upper atmosphere where it can shield the earth below from the direct rays of the sun for prolonged periods of time. It is difficult to do more than theorize about volcanism as a cause of change of climate, however, since there is no way at present to date the volcanic explosions and equate them with the variations in temperature.

It will be noted that volcanism is not only a crustal theory but also an atmospheric hypothesis since the eruptions changed the nature of the sea of air in which the world is bathed. There are also pure atmospheric theories. Without being related directly to changes in the crust, it is possible that the carbon-dioxide content of the air may have been changed, and this would be very significant. All geophysicists are aware that life as we know it today is possible on earth only because we have carbon dioxide in the atmosphere. This gas serves as a blanket to protect us from some of the damaging rays of the sun and reflects back some of the heat which the earth releases. Were it not for the "greenhouse" effect of the carbon dioxide, we would have some of the temperature extremes said to exist on the moon.

If carbon dioxide is that important, it follows that perhaps in the past, as a result of variations in animal or vegetable combustion, we were provided with superior or inferior "greenhouses." Indeed, this is entirely possible, but further complications must be introduced. The oceans store the gas very efficiently, and a circulatory cycle that takes tens of thousands of years carries carbon dioxide–rich or –poor water from the surface to the bottom and back to the surface again. Thus, whatever is happening to the balance as a result of land processes is modified by the ocean-reservoir migrations.

With temperature changes resulting from changes in carbon dioxide, there must be changes simultaneously in cloud cover. And the clouds, themselves, serve as sun shields and modify the water cycle: reducing evaporation and increasing precipitation. All in all, the complexity involved with this theory is rather greater than can be handled satisfactorily.

Up to this point, theories that affect solar radiation indirectly have been discussed. There are obviously those who say "Don't bother with these secondary processes. Let's look at changes in the sun itself." The scientists who prefer to view the problem from this angle have created a variety of astronomical hypotheses.

As far as is known, the radiation coming from the sun is very constant except for the occasional solar flare, which occurs sporadically and interferes with radio communication. There are periods of sunspot maxima and minima but these are known to occur in eleven- and twenty-three-year cycles. Despite the present constancy, it is not unreasonable to suppose, however, that occasionally the sun, as it travels in its own orbit through our galaxy, may intercept clouds of intersteller dust. This type of collision would produce a marked change in solar radiation and could explain all the climatic changes known. But have these collisions occurred, and when did they occur?

And speaking of orbits, the earth's orbit around the sun changes with time as does the inclination of the earth's axis with respect to its orbit. The ellipse that describes the earth's motion around its personal star seemed to breathe, alternately flattening and rounding out in a process taking about 90,000 years per inhalation-exhalation. Computations show that there would be an increase of 20 per cent in the amount of radiation received when the earth is closest to the sun over that received when it is farthest away. The wobble of the earth on its axis has a period of approximately 45,000 years. Since it is this angle of the earth to the orbit that is responsible for the progression of our seasons, this oscillation will alternately tend to wipe out the seasons and exaggerate them.

In explaining what has happened in the past, any one or more of these hypotheses may be used according to the predilections of the user. The simple fact is that no one really knows, and it seems unlikely that we shall get a definitive explanation in the near future. Is our climate changing? Without knowing why climate changes, this question cannot be answered. Each of us, relying upon his own experience and temperament, can feel free to adopt any position he chooses.

This type of discussion is not an exercise in futility, despite the fact that we walk along numerous avenues all ending nowhere. Although none of these has led to the destination we sought, they all have contributed greatly to a general knowledge and understanding of atmospheric processes. Moreover, and this is a factor not to be ignored by any meteorologist, a discussion such as this again emphasizes the extraordinary complexities of atmospheric science. Meteorologists are not necessarily dolts just because they cannot answer a quasi-simple question about our changing climate.

6

The Wind Doth Blow

Inevitably, the progress man makes in his various scientific endeavors is a direct function of the ease with which he can manipulate the factors determining the sciences he is exploring. The tremendous advances in physics are not only a tribute to man's ingenuity but also to the relative simplicity of many of the laws governing physical behavior. It is not a difficult step to go from the dropping of two objects of different weight from the Leaning Tower of Pisa to repeating the same experiment in a vacuum and establishing the gravitational constant. When all or most of the influencing variables are subject to laboratory control, the bits and pieces from which scientific laws are deduced can be isolated. When the various factors are difficult or impossible to isolate, the laws are harder to come by. Thus, there is a progressive decrease in knowledge as one goes from physics and chemistry through the biological disciplines to the geophysical sciences as fewer and fewer experiments can be performed in the laboratory and more and more factors defy identification and control.

Despite all the unknowns about the atmosphere, some of which have just been indicated, there are large areas where much is known. Let us shift from considering atmospheric questions for which few if any answers can be found to aspects of weather that are well understood and for which we can describe a satisfactory mechanism.

Let us consider the winds that blow over the earth—all types of winds from the kind which are global in nature, such as the trade winds and the Roaring Forties, to the very local winds, such as the sea breeze enjoyed by vacationers on a hot summer's day as long as they remain within a few miles of the coast.

No difficult natural laws govern the movement of air on any scale and it is relatively simple to give the rules that must be applied for explanation. Cold air is more dense than warm air so that, given an opportunity, cold air will always push its way under the warm, replacing it at the surface and pushing it aloft. "Nature abhors a vacuum" and "warm air rises" are both explained by this characteristic. And then there is the Coriolis force, which was considered earlier, that seems to shove all air currents to the right in the northern hemisphere.

The third fact that must be considered is the manner by which the air acquires the temperature it possesses—the source and utilization of heat energy. All heat comes from the sun initially. Where the sun shines at right angles to the earth, its effect is the greatest, not only because it is concentrated on a smaller area of the earth's surface but also because it traverses a smaller path through the shielding atmosphere. The nature of the surface on which solar energy impacts also makes its contribution toward temperature differences. Land, and particularly land not covered by dense vegetation, receives the energy on its topmost layer and keeps it there. Heat can only be transferred downward by conduction—a slow process. As a result, land surfaces heat rapidly in sunlight but cool just as rapidly after the sun goes down. Anyone who enjoys walking barefoot in the sand at the beach can attest to that fact.

By contrast, the ocean acts as a great reservoir of heat. Because of its motion, the water does not tend to store its heat in the top layer, and thus, when the depth is sufficient, the heat received gradually warms the entire body of water. Since the mass of water is so vast, there is very little temperature change. In the same way, water does not cool very rapidly either. As the surface layer loses heat, it becomes more dense and sinks, being replaced by warmer water below. The ocean is a giant thermostatic bath that manages, for long periods of time, to maintain a more or less uniform temperature.

With these basic facts and neglecting secondary ones involving centrifugal forces, friction, and so forth, it is possible to visualize almost all the wind actions with which we are acquainted. Let us consider the circulation of air over the globe first and account for the doldrums, the horse latitudes, the trade winds, and the westerlies about which one always hears and reads. The air over the equator derives the greatest benefit from the solar radiation. It heats up, becomes less dense, and is readily pushed upward by cooler air from either side of the equator. The flow of this cooler air at the surface, with its deflection to the west because of the earth's spin, becomes the trade winds that render the northern shores of tropical islands such as Puerto Rico so much more comfortable than the southern. Aloft, where the equatorial air has been pushed up and away are the antitrades blowing from the southwest in the northern hemisphere and the northwest in the southern. In the region of rising hot, humid air, frequent rain showers combine with the heat and humidity to create the doldrums.

However, the air, in rising, expands and cools so that somewhere, as it moves northward, it encounters air of substantially the same, or even lower, density. Where this happens, a part of the current of air aloft, called the antitrades, flows back to the surface again. Usually, this happens near latitudes

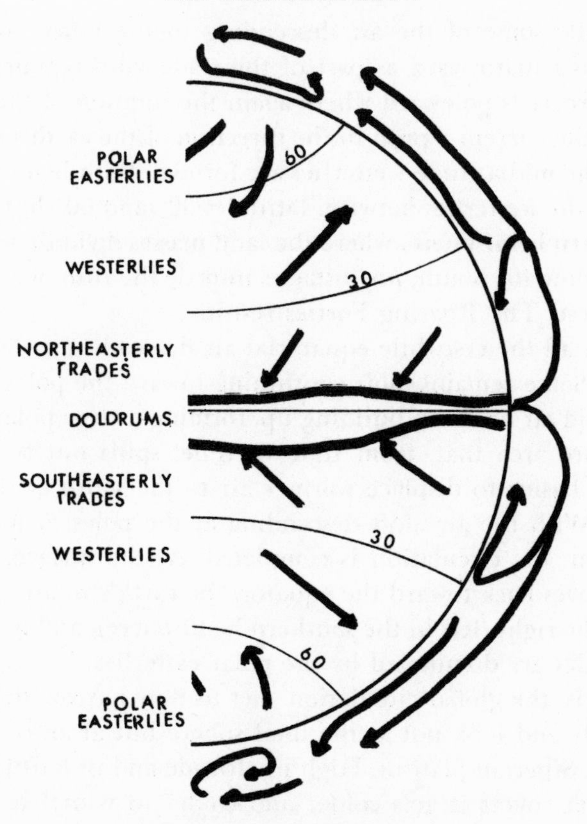

Global Circulation

30° north and south, where the descending air builds up a high-pressure belt at the surface. Having lost its moisture earlier, it creates a wide band of warm, cloudless skies—the horse latitudes, as our grandfathers called them and the Bermuda High, as more sophisticated East Coast residents call one section of this belt now. Here exist the prolonged calms that beset the sailing vessels in days past and where now we enjoy the mild, sunny climate of subtropical vacation resorts.

While some of the air descending in the horse latitudes returns equatorward as part of the trade-wind regime, some also proceeds poleward where again the rotation of the earth gives the current a push in the direction of the earth's spin so that the midlatitude westerlies are formed. Both hemispheres know the westerlies between latitudes 30° and 60° but in the southern hemisphere, where the land masses dwindle to nothing below 40° South, no obstacles impede the rush of air from the west. The Roaring Forties result.

Not all the erstwhile equatorial air descends near 30° latitude. Some remains aloft continuing toward the poles where the cold air has been building up, forming a large polar high-pressure area that, from time to time, spills out from the arctic basins to displace warmer air to the south at the surface. With the air aloft descending at the poles to join this current, the circulation is completed. At the surface, as the air moves back toward the equator, the earth's rotation turns it to the right (left in the southern hemisphere), and northern latitudes are dominated by the polar easterlies.

Thus, the global circulation. Let us now narrow the focus slightly and look not at the total sphere but at an octant of it: the Siberian plateau. High in altitude and in latitude, the air that covers it gets colder and colder in winter as it lies quietly in its great basin. Eventually, however, the basin gets filled to overflowing. This usually occurs in midwinter. The cold air then spills out, moving southward and downward toward the warm Indian Ocean. As it flows toward the southwest, it covers India with clear, dry air and the winter monsoon is in progress. This process is so regular that residents of the subcontinent speak of the monsoon being early or late in a given year.

In summer, the reverse temperature regime prevails. The large Siberian land mass heats, forming a low-pressure area. Now the air flow goes in the opposite direction producing a stream of moist air from the ocean over India toward Siberia. This air is moisture-laden from its oceanic source, and as it travels northward, climbing the terrain, it cools, condensing and precipitating the water it carried as vapor. The monsoon of July brings clouds and heavy rains to India. Over eighty inches of rain fall annually in parts of Southeast Asia and the greater part can be attributed to the monsoon.

The North American continent also knows a monsoonal circulation, but the basin in northwest Canada is so much smaller and so poorly protected by obstructions to the east and south that the build-ups and breakdowns of the temperature regimes are much less pronounced. The savage cold weather that comes down over the plain states in winter and the humid, hot air that blankets the same region in summer are both North American monsoons, however.

On a very small scale, "monsoons" can be observed at any beach during almost any twenty-four-hour period in the summer. During the day, the land gets warmer than the water until the contrast is sufficient to permit the cooler off-shore

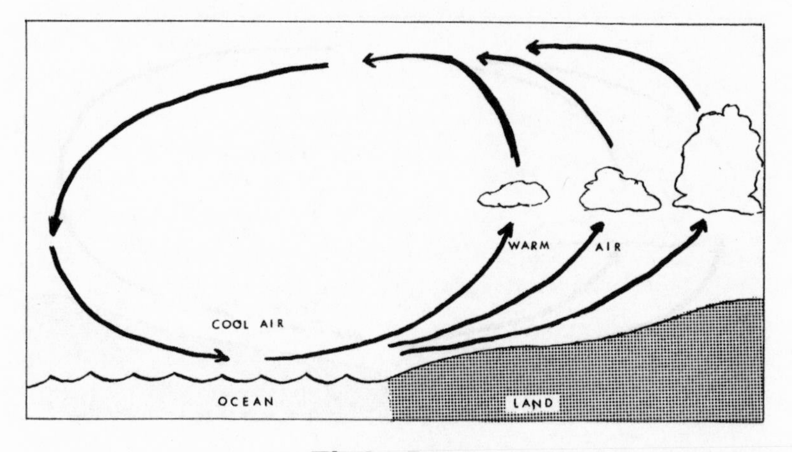

The Sea Breeze

air to flow in to shore, replacing the land-baked air at the coast. An eddy builds up that may reach a horizontal dimension of some twenty-five miles on a very hot day. Fair-weather cumulus forming in the rising air over the shore line gives notice to the roasted city dwellers driving to the beach of the prospect of sudden relief that will be found in the ten- to twenty-degree temperature drop as they reach the shore area.

When the sun goes down, the sea breeze, as this miniscule monsoon is called, breaks down but is soon replaced by its counterpart, the land breeze. In a quick reversal after sundown, the land area cools by radiation, achieving temperatures substantially less than the constant water temperature. Cool air now flows from land to ocean. The vacationer at the beach can brag to his friends at home about needing a blanket while he sleeps.

This boast can be topped with ease by the summer traveler who goes to the mountains. His postcards home can truthfully report that he requires three blankets for nighttime comfort. At night, the slopes of the mountains give off much

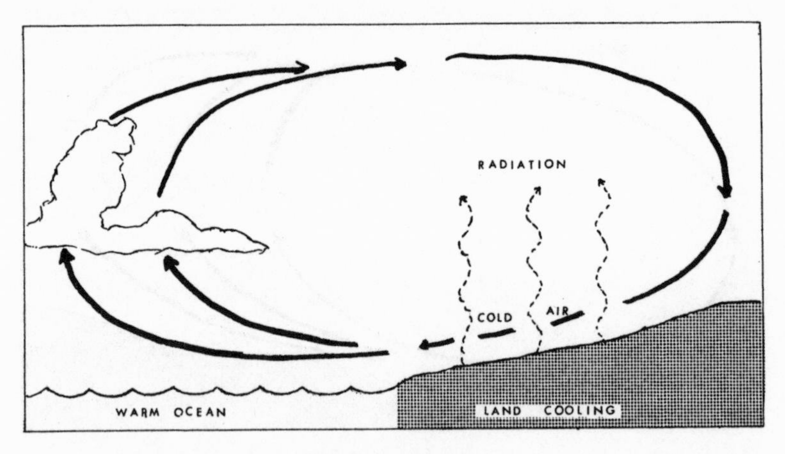

The Land Breeze

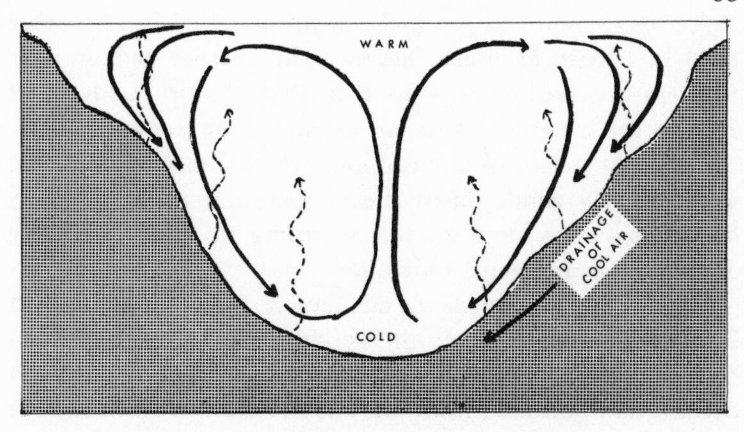

The Valley Wind

of the heat acquired during the day, and the air resting on them cools rapidly. The colder the air, the more dense it becomes, and substances of greater density displace those of lesser density. Thus, the cool air from the slopes slides down the mountainsides forcing the warmer air in the valley aloft. A circulation is set up producing a wind flow called "katabatic" by atmospheric scientists, a word derived from the Greek *katabainein*, meaning "going down." Regardless of the technical word, the general effect of these local circulations is exceedingly pleasant.

Not all of these local winds are pleasant, however. There is a family of them that may be beneficial but may also bring unpleasantness and destruction in its wake. The name by which each variety is called depends upon the location. In the northwestern part of the United States, it is known as a chinook, while in southern California, a particularly virulent form is called the Santa Ana. The *zonda* of Argentina, the *austru* of Rumania, and the *aspre* of central France are other names for this wind, although the term most often used by scientists in referring to this phenomenon is "foehn wind."

A classic case of such a foehn wind occurred in December 1933 in Havre, Montana. Severe cold weather had brought temperatures as low as −13°F to that region. Suddenly at 7:19 in the evening, when the thermometer stood at −9°F, "almost like a shot from a cannon," the chinook hit, and the southwesterly winds raised the temperature instantaneously to +18° with a more gradual warming to +44° following during the next twenty-four hours.

What had happened? A change in wind direction had brought the air, not from the neighboring plains, but down the mountain slopes to the west of Havre. Each 1,000 feet of descent had warmed the air another 5.5°F since air heats as it moves downward toward higher atmospheric pressures. In a steady tide, it poured over Havre creating the abnormal December temperature reading.

In this case, the chinook was undoubtedly welcomed, and, indeed, it is often awaited eagerly in winter to provide relief from the worst winter weather. A well-known painting by Charles M. Russell in 1886 depicts this interesting aspect. He called it "Waiting for a Chinook." At the time, he was an unknown "range rider" working for Stadler and Kaufman, two large cattlemen. During the winter of 1886, a very severe snowstorm struck Montana, covering the entire area with such a heavy blanket of snow that cattle and sheep literally died by the thousands. Russell's employers, alarmed by the weather reports, wrote to inquire about the condition of their herds. Rather than answer by letter, Russell chose to sketch the water color showing the coyotes waiting for the last victims of the storm. The title of the picture is obviously derived from Russell's awareness that the snow cover could be melted rapidly only by the development of a chinook.

While the tempering of an arctic climate can only be considered desirable, many who are subjected to these foehn winds complain bitterly of considerable physical discomfort.

Charles M. Russell's "Waiting for a Chinook"

European literature contains numerous descriptions of so-called foehn sickness. Low spirits, general ill-being, and depression, accompanied by many suicides, muscular convulsions, and heart disturbances are reported as coinciding with the advent of foehn winds. Elaborate studies have attempted to correlate these symptoms with such meteorological elements as pressure pulsations, increased oxygen, decreased water vapor, or the possible presence of noxious gas. No specific relation seems to exist. Interestingly enough, the illness is felt as keenly by those in carefully closed rooms as by those in exposed places and, in the United States, no one has complained of foehn sickness.

Under certain conditions, the foehn wind can have a much more disastrous effect—even in this country. This happens when the flow off the mountains is obstructed and the wind is forced through a narrow pass or canyon. Now, in addition to the heat and the dryness, there is the wind to cope with, for the air may flow at a speed approaching ninety miles per hour.

A friend of mine, a Wave officer, Lt. Marguerite Hunold, won a decoration for forecasting one of these winds. She was stationed at Klamath Falls, Oregon, where for many weeks she was the only weather officer at the Naval Air Facility. Day in and day out, weekdays, Sundays, and holidays, she was on duty, taking her sleep in snatches in order to provide the many forecasts required by the pilots and others at that location. At long last, another weather officer reported for duty: a young man fresh out of school without any practical weather experience.

Another week was devoted to breaking the newcomer into the weather-office routine and then, with a relatively quiet week end in prospect, Lt. Hunold felt that she could take a couple of days off. She did not feel sufficiently secure, however, to leave the station. All day Saturday she restrained herself from going to the weather office, realizing that her junior officer had to learn independence and responsibility. On Sunday morning, however, she dropped in to see how everything was going.

First, she looked at the posted forecast, which indicated that a clear day with winds between 15 and 20 miles per hour would prevail. She then stepped over to the analyzed weather chart, studied it for a moment and dashed for the telephone.

She called the officer of the day. "I'd advise you to put the storm bill into effect," she told him. "You had better secure all flying and get the planes in hangars or lashed down."

It was the commanding officer who walked into the office a few minutes later. "What's all this?" he wanted to know.

"I expect winds in excess of 50 knots within the next few hours."

The captain looked from the window at the clear sky and mildly fluttering flag. "Over fifty knots?" Each word emphasized his disbelief.

"I'll put it in writing," the Wave officer told him.

Convinced that no action was required, but unwilling to ignore the warning given by his weather officer, he ordered the storm bill put into effect and watched the airfield come alive with activity as everything movable was shifted to shelter or securely tied down to withstand the blast of a high wind. Yet, everything was balmy at Klamath Falls and remained so for another hour.

Then, slowly, the wind picked up. On the anemometer dial, the needle started to climb. At first, it inched up, but having started its way across the dial, it accelerated, eventually reaching 70 miles per hour. Aircraft parked on the field strained at their ropes trying desperately to tear loose. A few signs labeling the post exchange and the gymnasium blew off and swept into the surrounding woods, but no major damage was sustained. By late afternoon, it was over, and the wind had again settled down to its 15 to 20 miles per hour.

My friend had noted the wind direction and, being well-acquainted with the configuration of the terrain in the vicinity, had judged that the air would be forced through one of the mountain passes in much the same way that water shoots through the nozzle of a high-pressure hose.

Had this happened in southern California, it would have been called a Santa Ana, but, as far as I know, there is no special term used for this wind in Oregon. In the Golden Gate State, the strong, hot, dry winds are often responsible for devastating fires, and it was in 1880 that an article in the Los Angeles *Evening Express*, discussing such a holocaust in Santa Ana, first gave the disastrous wind the name of that town.

At any rate, unless a forecaster is intimately acquainted with the topography around his location, he cannot be expected to predict a Santa Ana. Such a forecast requires a special local experience—and sometimes a considerable amount of courage.

7

Weather Lore and Science

A manned satellite was launched this morning, and in homes, offices, and workshops, we watched our TV screens breathlessly as the huge rocket assembly ignited, rising ponderously to carry the precious capsule into the sky. When the fiery streak dwindled to nothingness as it outdistanced even the most powerful camera zoom lens, and the commentator announced that a successful orbit had been achieved, we settled back relieved and proud of our accomplishment. Our accomplishment!

The vast majority of us in this fantastic, technologically advanced civilization cannot adjust a carburetor on our ubiquitous cars and lawn mowers, have not the vaguest idea of the nature of the aspirins or tranquilizers that we swallow by the millions, or the manner by which the electrical genie serves every need of home or factory. An interesting and humbling pastime involves the supposition that one is miraculously transported backward in time to the year 1700. Assuming that no hostility is encountered and fullest cooperation accorded, how much of the wonders of the latter half of the twentieth century could any of us bestow upon the people of that earlier age?

As members of the general populace, we take inordinate

personal pride in the specialized knowledge of a few in our midst, accepting their accomplishments as our own. Yet we tend to discount entirely the very considerable body of useful and accurate knowledge that was accumulated by our ancestors. True enough, they often were unable to systematize facts into a cohesive whole; their attempts at explanation of what they observed seem ludicrously naive and erroneous in the light of modern knowledge, but their observations were frequently accurate and detailed. Even today, our explanations of what is occurring are only theories or hypotheses subject to change without notice. Even so-called physical laws are not immutable. Within the lifetime of many of us, the Law of Conservation of Mass had to be modified to read the Law of Conservation of Mass-Energy.

Not only are we not so smart in an absolute sense, but also we are not so smart relative to our ancestors. Take meteorology, for example, which is credited as being a really modern science. While pioneers in physics invented such instruments as the barometer and the thermometer at earlier dates, the first weather map was not drawn until the year 1820. Supposedly, a decade or so earlier Napoleon had suffered a disastrous setback as the result of the advent of a sudden storm and had detailed someone the task of determining whether such a storm was predictable. Weather information was collected from a considerable area in Europe, with the result that the presence of a pattern and a more or less orderly progression in weather was recognized. W. H. Brandes, using a notation all his own, consolidated this type of information on a map in 1820, producing the first progenitor of the modern weather map.

It was not until shortly after World War I that V. Bjerknes introduced the frontal theory of atmospheric behavior. The United States Weather Bureau has been basing its forecasts on this concept of warring polar and tropical air masses for only some three decades.

This makes weather science new in any historical sense. Yet, it is perhaps only the theories and explanations that are truly new. Many of the observations and their significance have been with us, not for decades, but for centuries and millenia.

> Above the rest, the sun who never lies
> Foretells the change of weather in the skies.

Virgil said, and many centuries later, in Act III of *Richard II,* Shakespeare also spoke of weather forecasts.

> Men judge by the complexion of the sky
> The state and inclination of the day.

In *Venus and Adonis,* he is more specific:

> A red morn, that ever yet betoken'd
> Wrack to the seaman, tempest to the field,
> Sorrow to shepherds, woe unto the birds:
> Gusts and foul flaws to herdmen and to herds.

This is weather forecasting in the true sense of the word, but, of course, the fact that a red sunrise augured a stormy day was not original with Shakespeare. This concept was carried by proverbs and adages through the ages and may even be found in the New Testament, in Matthew 16, together with a companion fact concerning red sunsets.

> He answered and said unto them, When it is evening, ye say, It will be fair weather: for the sky is red. And in the morning, It will be foul weather today: for the sky is red and lowering. O ye hypocrites, ye can discern the face of the sky; but can ye not discern the signs of the times?

The encyclopedic Shakespeare knew about red sunsets, too. In *Richard II*, he has Richmond say:

> The weary sun hath made a golden set,
> And by the bright tracks of his fiery car
> Gives token of a goodly day tomorrow.

Several dozen folk sayings reveal that for centuries people have watched the rising and setting sun in order to determine the next day's weather. To give just a few:

> If the sun set in grey
> The next will be a rainy day.
>
> If the sun goes pale to bed
> 'Twill rain tomorrow, it is said.
>
> If red the sun begin his race
> Be sure the rain will fall apace.
>
> Sky red in the morning
> Is a sailor's sure warning;
> Sky red at night
> Is the sailor's delight.
>
> Evening grey and morning red
> Make the shepherd hang his head.
>
> Evening red and morning grey
> Two sure signs of one fine day.

These simple statements, such as those from the New Testament and from Shakespeare, are easy to explain since they involve mainly the recognition that in our latitudes weather travels largely from west to east. When the sun is just below the horizon, the colors of a sunrise or sunset are most vivid in the sky opposite. The thundering drama of a sunrise, with its interplay of reds, golds, purples, and saffron is staged on the cloudy proscenium of the western sky. The clear weather to the east, which licensed the appearance of the star before its vast audience, will be followed in due course by the pit-pattering of the weeping cloudy chorus as it makes its way to center stage.

Thus, the matinee. The evening's performance, reversing the position of the backdrop, admits the sun from the west, playing the spectral lights on weather that has passed.

The doubled requirements such as:

Evening red and morning grey
Help the traveler on his way;
Evening grey and morning red
Bring down rain upon his head.

require a somewhat more involved explanation, since the reasons for morning or evening grey are not quite as obvious.

For the explanation of the former, we must look to radiational cooling, as we did earlier for the cause of land and valley breezes. The origin of these sayings in English folklore (rather than American) gives another clue, for England is traditionally the location of radiation fogs. The cooling that occurs on a clear, windless night will often reduce the temperature of the air enough to produce some condensation so that a shallow layer of ground fog appears before dawn. As soon as the sun rises, this will be burned off again, and the clear, cloudless sky will be revealed, but until the heat of the sun has become appreciable, the misty blanket shields the celestial dome from the searching eye of the shepherd, the sailor, or the traveler. Morning grey is often a welcome presage of things to come.

On the other hand, when the western sky is banked with clouds that obscure the setting sun or obstruct the usual color progression when the sun's rays make a prism of the atmosphere as the glowing ball falls below the horizon, we have evening grey. The clouds in the west betoken the advent of bad weather which, if it has not arrived during the night, is further prophesied by the ruddy sunrise.

Since a rainbow is always formed in the direction opposite to the sun, whose rays are diffracted by prismatic water drops, the use of the rainbow as a forecasting tool is reasonably straightforward.

> If there be a rainbow in the eve,
> It will rain and leave;
> But if there be a rainbow in the morrow
> It will neither lend nor borrow.
>
> Rainbow at night, shepherd's delight.
> Rainbow in morning, shepherds take warning.

Even more direct is the relationship between the storm and the wind:

> Rainbow to windward, foul falls the day;
> Rainbow to leeward, damp runs away.

The moon, too, brings its portents with occasional haloes and coronas.

> The moon with a circle brings water in her beck.
>
> When the wheel is far, the storm is n'ar;
> When the wheel is n'ar, the storm is far.
>
> If the moon show a silver shield,
> Be not afraid to reap your field;
> But if she rises haloed round,
> Soon we'll tread on deluged ground.

Particularly with the advance of warm fronts and hurricanes, a cloud shield moves in ahead of the area of bad weather. First, very high in the sky come the thin, feathery cirrus clouds composed of a scattering of ice crystals. These clouds are the "mare's tails" or "painter's brush" of popular lore. They are not contiguous enough to obscure the moon whose rays are diffracted as they traverse the ice crystals and form a halo.

> Mackerel sky and mare's tails
> Make tall ships carry low sails.
>
> Trace in the sky the painter's brush
> The winds around you soon will rush.

The ring around the moon gives evidence of the unseen clouds and first notice of what is now called a warm front but which our forefathers called, indiscriminately, bad weather.

As the front comes closer, the clouds gradually thicken and lower. No longer is diffraction by ice crystals apparent. Instead, clouds composed of liquid-water drops refract the light rays, and a corona circles the moon until the clouds become so thick as to obscure all view of the earth's natural satellite. The lower the clouds, the larger the ring and the nearer the zone of bad weather.

Since it is, in general, warm frontal conditions that bring rain of longest duration—unlike the cold front which is a narrow band of bad weather or the summer's thunderstorm, which quickly spends its violence—these circular omens about the moon betoken prolonged periods of stormy weather. In folklore:

> Rain long foretold, long last;
> Short notice, soon past.

So much valuable weather information was known to our progenitors. The modern weather forecaster uses much of this information identically, even though he can no longer quote the folk sayings. When it comes to the determination of early morning temperature, the forecaster carefully considers the cloud cover. In the absence of cloud to return nighttime radiation from the ground back to earth, the temperature drops sharply. In spring or fall, a frost forecast must be considered on every clear night.

Clear moon, frost soon.

Even if the temperature at ground level does not drop to the freezing point it may easily fall sufficiently to produce condensation of the humid air, resulting in dew. Thus, the presence of early morning dew bespeaks of the previous night's cloudless sky.

When the grass is dry at morning light
Look for rain before the night.
When the dew is on the grass
Rain will never come to pass.

When the morn is dry,
The rain is nigh.
When the morn is wet,
No rain you get.

The wind direction and particularly its changes are still vitally important indices to modern meteorologists. In the absence of pressure disturbances, as we have seen from the general circulation, the winds in middle latitudes are westerly. As a weather disturbance forms upwind, because of the counterclockwise circulation around the low center, the winds "back," shifting from westerly to southwesterly and southerly. As the disturbance, be it a cyclonic center or a cold front, drifts toward the east, the winds return to westerly again or "veer." The forecaster now, as well as in the past, gives considerable weight to the wind although at present it is done less poetically.

When the smoke goes west,
Gude weather is past;
When the smoke goes east,
Gude weather comes neist.

When the wind backs and weatherglass falls
Then be on your guard against gales and squalls.

When the wind is in the south
The rain's in its mouth.
The wind in the west
Suits everyone best.

To me the most fascinating adages are the ones that, at present, only a few atmospheric investigators can readily explain. These researchers have been concentrating on indirect means of probing the upper atmosphere. Instead of sending instruments aloft on balloons or rockets, they have been exploring through the use of sound and radio waves. It is from this background that they understand what the couplets that follow have to say. Our great grandparents knew about the way sound travels and interpreted what they heard correctly.

Sound traveling far and wide
A stormy day will betide.

When the peacock loudly bawls
Soon we'll have both rain and squalls.

Our fathers and grandfathers, however, all but forgot the use of sound in assessing the atmosphere, although they had more opportunity than others, before or after, to make the necessary observations and deductions. World War I, fought in Flanders and northeastern France with howitzers, mortars, and railway guns, with tremendous artillery barrages prior to each effort to change the position of entrenched soldiers a

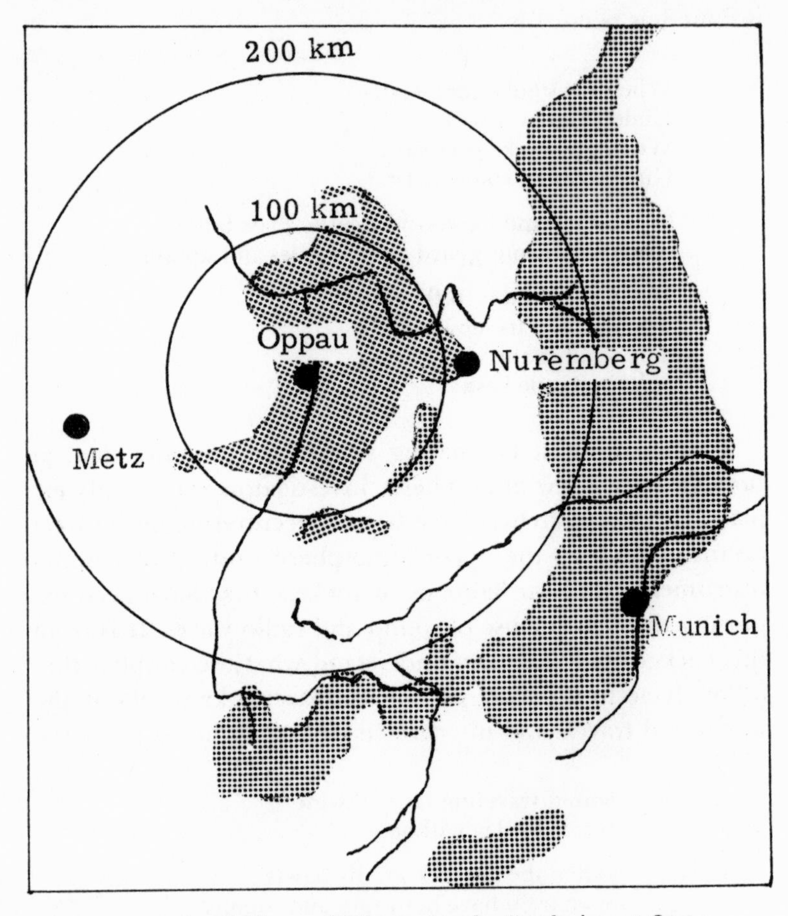

Zones of Audibility and Silence for the Explosion at Oppau, Germany, on September 21, 1921

few hundred feet, provided, perhaps, the most sustained, loud, localized sources of sound known to man. Deafening as the volume must have been to the men dug into the mud at Verdun, St. Quentin, and Chateau Thierry, it could not be expected that the sound of battle would carry as far as

England, for example. Yet, on occasion, Londoners heard the barrages, and windows rattled in the English countryside ninety or more miles away from the exploding shells.

By means of door-to-door surveys, on several of the days when the sound traveled unbelievable distances, the general pattern of zones of audibility and inaudibility were established. Immediately around the battle zone, the booming could be heard directly, as we hear the backfire of a car down the road. Gradually, with increasing distance, the sound diminished, until at the fringes whether or not it was heard depended upon the keenness of the ears of the people listening, their preoccupation with other business, and the general level of local noise in their vicinity. Beyond, no one heard the guns for many miles but then, at a much more considerable distance, the booming could be heard again by all except the deaf.

This sound did not travel directly in a straight line from explosion to ear. It went up into the atmosphere and, in a long curving path, was returned to earth again. How did this happen, and why on some days and not on others?

Sound travels at a greater speed in warm air than in cool. Imagine a line that is the "sound front" leaving the earth at an angle and heading into the sky. If the temperature were everywhere the same, this front would continue advancing, straight and unaltered, to the boundaries of outer space. If the temperature always decreased with height, the top part of the rising sound front would travel just a little more slowly than the lower part so that the angle of the line would change gradually, and, instead of maintaining its uniform course, the sound front would shift more and more nearly parallel to the surface with the sound traveling more nearly directly upward.

If the temperature increases with height for a considerable layer, as it does with an approaching warm front, the upper part of the advancing sound beam travels faster than its lower counterpart, and, instead of bending away from earth, the sound curves in the reverse direction, perhaps sufficiently to turn back toward the ground again. Thus, the guns fired in French battlefields could be heard in England.

In recent years, vast areas about a predetermined explosion site have been instrumented with sensitive microphones in an effort to learn more about temperatures and winds aloft. Winds enter the picture, too, since the second, or indirect, zone of audibility is not necessarily exactly concentric about the explosion. It is displaced downwind as the molecules of air, whose vibrations transmit the sound, are carried in the wind current.

At any rate, it was known and then forgotten that when sound traveled best, stormy weather could be anticipated. Only the explanation that it resulted from the overriding warm air preceding the arrival of a warm front was missing.

Interestingly enough, World War II also had its incidents

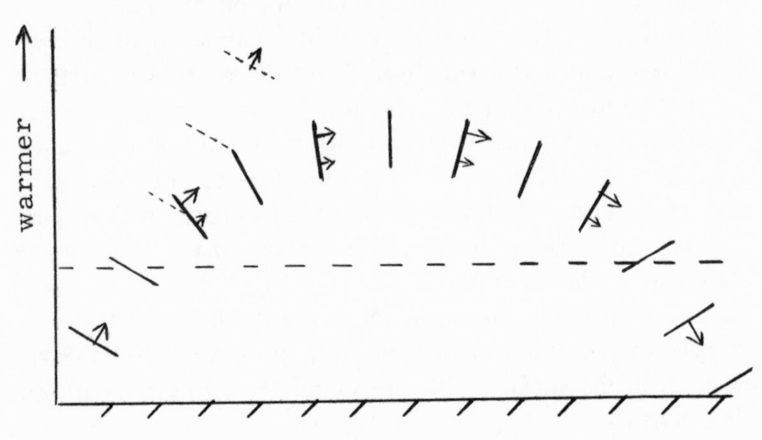

A Sound Beam Bends When It Encounters a Warmer Layer of Air Aloft

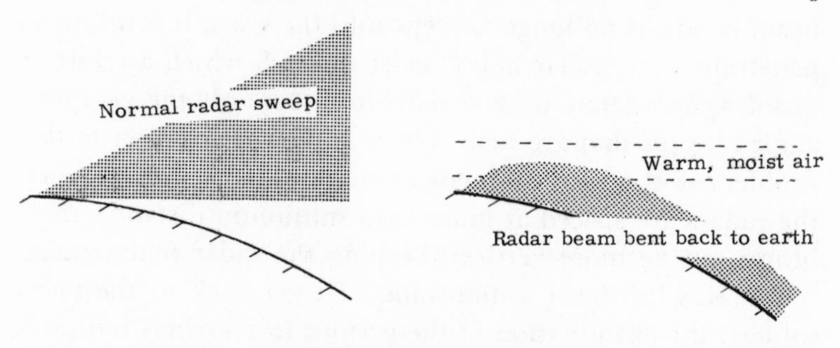

Bending of a Radar Beam

relating to the curving of rays in the warmer upper layers of the atmosphere, except that it was not sound but radar beams that bent back to earth. The search radar used in an effort to locate enemy shipping can normally not "see" what is happening at the earth's surface for more than thirty or forty miles (depending on the height of the antenna and the broadness of the beam) because the earth's surface is curved and drops away from a beam which is emitted parallel to the surface. But if the beam bends with the earth as a result of the temperature and moisture irregularities, the range at which the radar can see something at the surface is increased almost indefinitely. Unless the radar operator is very careful, he cannot always distinguish between a target within normal range and one that has come from great distances.

At least once during World War II, a United States Navy task force opened fire with its 16-inch guns on units of the Japanese fleet that were 400 miles away. The radar operator had not tested his targets for the possibility of skip distances.

The same phenomenon of the bending ray presents problems to the radar operators on the DEW line, our first line of defense against unexpected airborne attack, and to the men of the Federal Aviation Authority who attempt to keep aircraft under constant surveillance. When the outreaching beam bends, it no longer sweeps into the space it is meant to penetrate, and "radar holes" exist through which aircraft or missiles can operate undetected. Since it is only the very low-angled beams that are bent significantly, the solution to this problem is the establishment of more radar stations. When the radars are spaced at more than minimum distance, their beams can be more vertical, keeping the radar fence intact.

But this has been a digression. To get back to the main subject, the examination of the various folk sayings indicates that we are not really so very much smarter now than our forebears were. Indeed, when all the accumulated weather lore can be read in one succinct verse, one wonders whether we are at all more clever than its unknown author:

> Last night the sun went pale to bed.
> The moon in haloes hid her head.
> The boding shepherd heaves a sigh
> For see! a rainbow spans the sky;
> Hark how the chairs and tables crack!
> Old Betty's joints are on the rack;
> Her corns with shooting pains torment her,

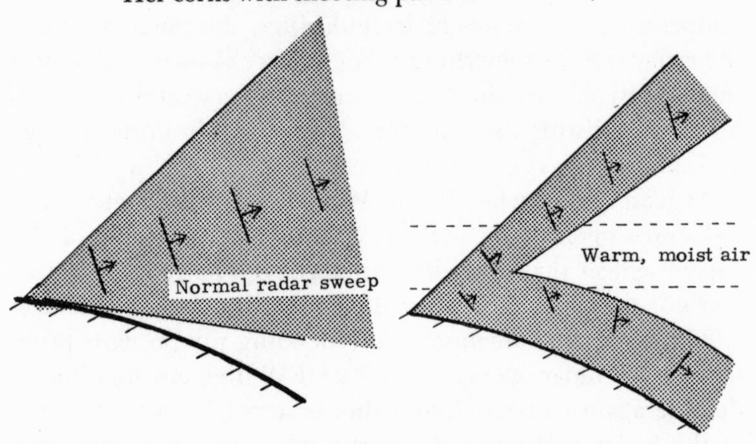

Development of a Radar Hole

And to bed untimely sent her;
Loud quack the ducks, the peacocks cry,
The distant hills are looking nigh;
How restless are the snorting swine!
The busy flies disturb the kine.
Low o'er the grass the swallow wings;
The cricket, too, how sharp he sings!
In fiery red, the sun doth rise,
Then wades through clouds to mount the skies.
"Twill surely rain—I see with sorrow,
Our jaunt must be put off tomorrow."

8

Battles of the Air

Having established that our forebears anticipated the frontal theory of weather development, we would probably do well to recap the essentials of that theory.

Let us start with a huge mass of air lying on the northwestern plateau of the North American continent in winter. For days, it has been covering the Canadian provinces of Alberta and Saskatchewan, getting colder as during each wintry night it radiates whatever heat it had through the cloudless sky while during each abbreviated day the glancing sun barely accords a tepid caress. The insulating white blanket covering the plateau spurns even this weak solar gesture by reflection while serving as a superior radiator during the long hours of darkness.

Day by day, the dome of air becomes more and more cold and ever deeper. The atmospheric pressure, which is nothing but the weight of air stretching in a column above, builds up, and the dome is clearly a high-pressure cell. The contrast between this mass of air and the much more moderate air to the south increases steadily until an intolerably unstable condition is created. It is as though oil and water or milk and cream were placed side by side in one container with the expectation that the lighter liquids would not float to the top changing a vertical separation to a horizontal one.

In the atmosphere, the action is not as simple as just a revision in the method of layering. There is no closed container with convenient walls to confine the movement. Only to the west, the range of the Rocky Mountains serves in this capacity. The cold, dense air, therefore, overflows its shallow bowl and flows southward and eastward. Some of the warm air in its path is pushed upward; some is pushed back. A boundary is formed between cold air and warmer air, and, since the cold air is advancing, the boundary is called a cold front or, more correctly, a cold frontal surface.

It is harder for the cold air to advance at the surface than aloft because friction slows the air down. Along the ground, it must fight for every inch of advance: across forests, hills, valleys, over every surface irregularity. The air above meets

A Cold Air Mass Spills over the Plain States

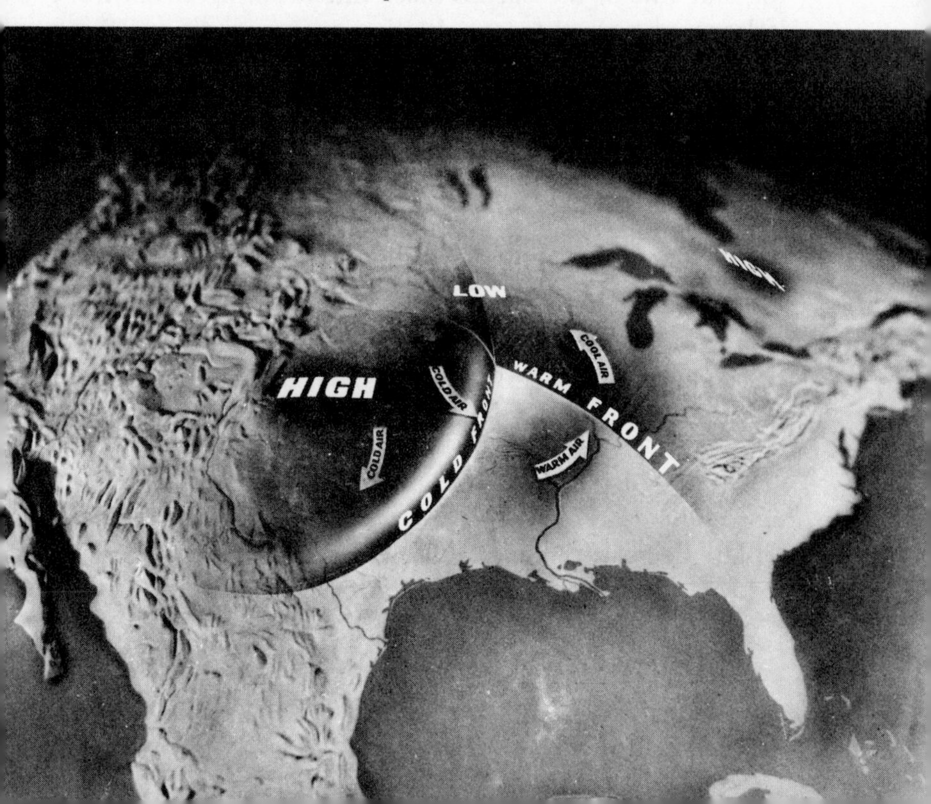

no such obstructions and can flow relatively freely, its only adversary being the warm air itself unabetted by terrestrial allies. The result of this difference in speed is the snub-nosed appearance of the cold front as seen in vertical profile.

How blunt the nose is depends upon the speed of advance of the cold air. Is the front moving rapidly or slowly? From the mechanics of the setup, it is apparent that the greater the speed, the greater will be the friction at the surface and therefore the greater the overhang of the cold air aloft. The entire frontal surface is more vertical with a rapidly advancing cold front. To give the picture some dimension: a really fast-moving cold front may have a slope of 1 in 40—that is, the boundary between cold air and warm air rises 1 mile for every 40 miles of horizontal extent.

At the surface there is, theoretically at least, a line where cold and warm air are in contact. This is the position where the blue line or the barbed black line denoting a cold front is drawn on a weather map showing surface conditions. Some 40 miles behind this position, to find the intersection of cold and warm air, it is necessary to climb about 5,000 feet, or 1 mile, vertically. If the weather map were drawn for the layer 5,000 feet up (an upper air chart), the cold front would be indicated 40 miles behind the surface front.

With a cold front moving rapidly enough to have a slope of 1 in 40, a squall line may very well be formed. This is a line of very severe weather that precedes the surface cold front. Examination of the behavior of both the warm air and the cold air in the vicinity of the frontal surface explains how this and other aspects of weather associated with a cold frontal passage come about.

As the cold air advances, the warm air is forced aloft. The more blunt the profile of the wedge of cold air, the more rapidly the warm must rise. With the front moving rapidly, the cold air above the surface can outdistance the friction-retarded air at the surface, forming an overhang. With this type of contour, there can be nothing gradual about the climb of the warm air. It must go straight up. If it is moisture-laden and unstable, perhaps having been saturated while it swept over the Gulf of Mexico, it will form tremendous vertical clouds, cumulonimbi, reaching as high as 40,000 feet perhaps, although this is more common with a squall line in seasons other than winter. When these clouds release their fury, hurling rain, lightning, and hail from their boiling centers, people below experience one of nature's extremes. The thunderstorms may well spawn tornadoes and floods. Thus, the passage of a squall line some twenty or more miles ahead of the surface front is more to be feared than the passage of the front itself.

The great slope of the fast-moving cold front also means that the bad weather is concentrated in a rather narrow zone. Whatever effect the rising warm air will have is achieved

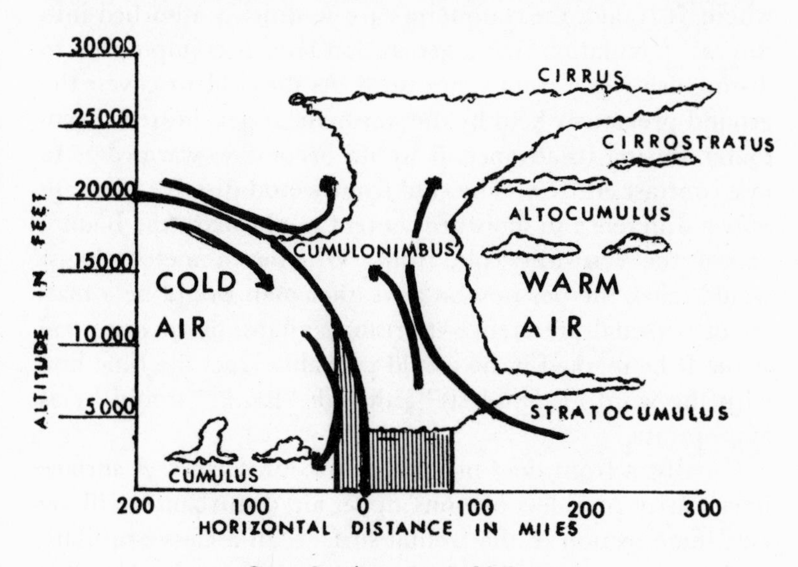

Cross Section of a Cold Front

rapidly. It is over and done with in one violent burst. By contrast, everything associated with a slow-moving cold front is more gradual. Rather than force its invasion of the territory held by the warm air in open battle, the cold mass insinuates its way forward using guerilla tactics. The slope of the frontal surface is smaller: 1 mile vertically for every 100 miles horizontally and there is no overhang with its accompanying squall line. With the more gradual slope, the displaced warm air is pushed upward out of the way less abruptly so that the weather it creates is not concentrated near the surface front. Clouds and rain can cover a much greater area behind the front. Instant good weather does not follow frontal passage when the cold front moves slowly.

If the terrain were reasonably smooth—no pronounced surface irregularity and no regions of greater or lesser heating—the cold front would advance steadily and uniformly. The eventual effect would be rather like an invasion of China where, it is said, the conquerors are so quickly absorbed into the vast population that a generation later it is impossible to distinguish victor from vanquished. As the cold air covers the ground previously held by the warm air, it gets heated. Eventually, during its advance, it would become so warmed as to lose contrast entirely. The cold front would dissolve. Perhaps only a difference in moisture content might mark the boundary of the erstwhile cold front. Whether a meteorologist would mark the position on a weather map would be a matter of personal preference—purism, perhaps, or an historical sense. If he marked it, he would probably label the blue line with the word "Frontolysis" although "R.I.P." would be as appropriate.

Usually, a front does not progress so uniformly. A surface irregularity or a less obvious upper-air disturbance will retard some section of the frontal surface. In a classic military maneuver, the flank pivots about the center and a "low" is formed. South and west of the low center, the flank continues to advance as a cold front. North and east, the winds no longer bombard the front on the cold-air side. The winds on the warm-air side continue their drive unabated, however. Now the vanquished becomes victor, as the warm air that had been retreating gains relative strength along the eastern part of the front, managing to check the cold-air army to make territorial gains of its own. The warm air advances. No longer do we have a cold front. It is a warm front.

The cold air retreats reluctantly, and the same frictional effect that rounded the advancing profile of the wedge of cold air earlier, now flattens the wedge as the mass in contact with the surface hangs on grimly to every nook and cranny which supplies a toehold. The slope of the warm frontal surface is only about 1 mile vertically to 150 miles horizontally. As the warm air slides up the inclined surface for as many as 500 miles, its moisture is gradually wrung out to form a continuous cloud deck: low clouds near the surface front and

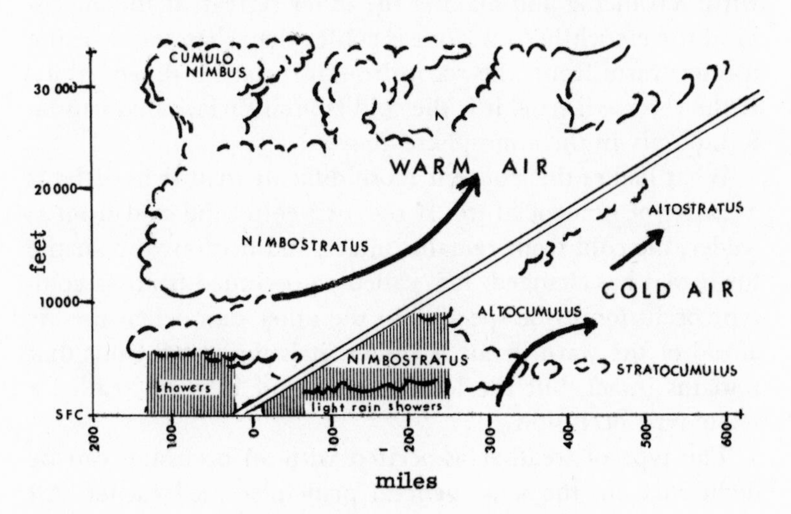

Cross Section of a Warm Front

higher and higher clouds over the cold air. If the warm air is unstable, thunderstorms form as well with bases hidden in the layer clouds, ready to trap the unwary pilot flying placidly in the calm, smooth clouds on either side.

There is no law saying that the two fronts, cold and warm, need travel at the same speed. Indeed, the cold front almost always moves faster, gaining on the warm and making the sector of warm air at the surface smaller and smaller. Eventually, the moment comes when the cold front catches up. When this happens, there are three frontal surfaces to be concerned about: an occluded front, which is the boundary between two masses of cold air, as well as the warm and cold fronts, which continue to mark the positions where the warm and cold air meet and struggle. The big difference is that the occluded front occupies the surface and low-altitude position. With all the warm air aloft, the cold and warm fronts are also aloft and nowhere touch the surface. At the surface, it is a battle between cold and colder air, and the colder air always wins: advancing and making the other retreat. If the air behind the erstwhile cold front is colder than that ahead of the former warm front, the warm frontal surface is shoved aloft. If the reverse is true, it is the cold frontal surface that can be found only in the atmosphere above.

What makes this concept more difficult than it need be is a matter of nomenclature. If the air behind the cold front is colder, the cold front remains intact, and it is only our name for it that has changed. It is called an occluded front—a cold-type occlusion to be specific. In the other case, when the air ahead of the warm front is colder, it is the warm front that remains intact, but the lower segment of it is now called a warm-type occlusion.

The type of weather associated with an occlusion can be deduced from the same general principles used earlier. All the warm air with its moisture is aloft where it can produce

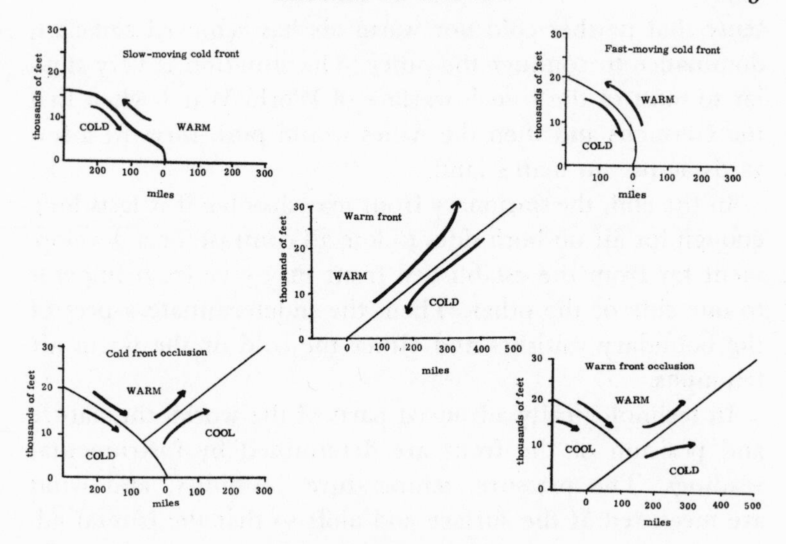

Typical Frontal Profiles

the clouds that are responsible for bad weather. Because of the geometry of the frontal surfaces, the bad weather is widespread. As a matter of passing interest, many a tourist in western Europe has noted the difference in weather there compared to that of the United States. Endless grey, rainy days are much more common abroad than at home. It should come as no surprise that many of the frontal systems leaving the East Coast of the United States occlude as they traverse the Atlantic and that a major source of bad weather in the British Isles and northern France is the occluded front.

One more type of front should be mentioned: the stationary front. On the weather map, if color is used, it is depicted by alternate red and blue segments; while in the black-and-white presentations, it is shown using alternate cold-front barbs and warm-front arcs. While the stationary front need not be truly static from a geographic point of view and may oscillate over a considerable region, it is stationary in the sense that neither cold nor warm air has achieved sufficient dominance to conquer the other. The situation is very similar to most of the trench warfare of World War I when first the Germans and then the Allies would push forward a few yards across no man's land.

In the end, the stationary front may dissolve if it lasts long enough for air on both sides to lose all contrast, or a development far from the established front may give fresh impetus to one side or the other. Then, the indeterminate aspect of the boundary vanishes and either the cold or the warm air triumphs.

In technologically advanced parts of the world, the nature and position of the front are determined by instrumental readings. The pressure, temperature, humidity, and wind are measured at the surface and aloft so that the frontal ad-

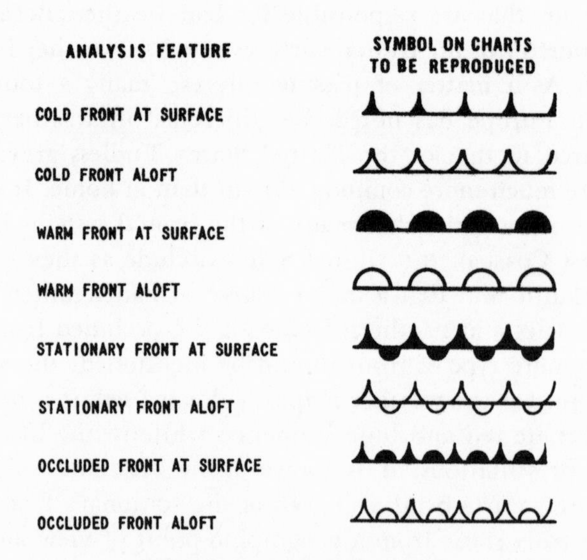

Weather Analysis Symbols

vance can be plotted exactly. In less-developed geographic areas, not only are the instruments and the means of communication absent, but people qualified to use the various pieces of equipment are not available even if these were supplied. Yet the more privileged population centers in these predominantly backward areas have need of weather forecasts. In past decades, in certain parts of the world cloud and precipitation patterns have proved reasonably satisfactory substitutes for numerical data in the drawing of weather maps. One of the balancing factors is the remarkable ability of primitive man to read the sky even if he cannot read a thermometer. Many a weather map of South America and Africa has been drawn using keen native observations to fill in for missing data.

Needless to say, instrumental data are more reliable than visual observations. Yet weather forecasting leaves much to be desired. Time and again, some one knowing of my interest in atmospheric behavior reminds me of the millions of dollars spent in collecting and transmitting data, adding: "It's still just a guessing game. For the past three days, they've been predicting showers and cooler weather. And it's just as hot as ever. Ever since they got that new man at the Weather Bureau. . . ."

It is difficult under such attack not to be arbitrarily defensive, and it is impossible to prove that the change of administrative head (or any individual) in a regional weather office cannot be solely responsible for busted forecasts. The fact of the matter is that almost all general forecasts issued to the public are based on predicted frontal movements. Sometimes, the fronts move decisively, and their rate of advance can be timed with great accuracy. Sometimes, the fronts move more erratically, so that their future course is more difficult or even impossible to predict.

It is rather like driving an automobile in a largely unpopulated country. If the tank is reasonably full of gasoline and your destination not too far, you can reliably forecast how long the trip will take. On the other hand, if the tank is low, the destination distant, and gas stations few and far between, it is almost impossible to predict how long the trip will last. As the fuel gets low and the engine begins to sputter, you may just manage to coast into a gas station, refill, and continue on your merry way. But perhaps the gas station is not there. Your car may come to a stop, leaving you to take a hike of indeterminate length before you can again move on.

A cold front approaching Washington, D.C., from the west must cross the Alleghany Mountains. If it has considerable impetus, it will do this easily, but if it does not have that full tank of fuel, it may have some difficulty. If it makes it, the temperature in Washington may drop 20°. If it does not, the heat wave continues unbroken. Sweltering Washingtonians looking hopefully at the little box in the upper lefthand corner of their morning newspaper (prepared at least six to twelve hours earlier) for a promise of relief can be quite unforgiving when the temperature, uninfluenced by the printed word, continues to soar. It is small comfort to them, too, that the front is stalled just a few miles away and that the cooler weather can be found in their neighbor's backyard if not in their own.

The weatherman's lament, of course, it that no one ever remembers all the forecasts he made correctly. But that is his problem. Let us get back to the business at hand. Blithely, thus far we have been accepting such statements as "if the air is unstable, a thunderstorm may develop" or "the stable air does not produce clouds." Just to round things out satisfactorily, it might be well to consider what is meant by atmospheric stability. There are a number of different kinds.

There is static stability. Something is statically stable when that which is heavier lies below that which is lighter. Thus, in the atmosphere, the proper order of things is for heavier, or more dense, air to lie below lighter, or less dense, air. Except for a very few desert locations, the atmosphere is always stable in this sense, and the atmosphere is always layered in terms of density. Over the desert, it is possible for the ground to heat up so much due to solar radiation that the layer of air heated by contact with the ground gets lighter than the air above it. This is instability, of course, and, like a child's top standing on its point without spinning, this condition can persist for only a very limited period of time. The slightest disturbance will upset the momentary, precarious balance and cause overturning whereby the warmer, less dense air assumes its proper position over the cooler, more dense air. The dust devils seen on a hot day in the desert give evidence of the adjustment of this type of instability.

In addition to static stability, there is a kind of stability that may be called dynamic. Our criterion here is what happens to a test object if we try to displace it. Will it resist displacement and, when released, return to its original position? If it does, it is dynamically stable or "absolutely stable." The best illustration of this is the child's round-bottomed doll. No matter how it is pushed, it oscillates for a little while and then returns to its erect position. It cannot be knocked over. It is absolutely or unconditionally stable.

Air can also be conditionally stable. To test the stability of a sample of air several things must be known about the column of atmosphere of which it is a part. We certainly must know the way temperature and humidity change with height, but let us consider only dry air for the moment. The variation of temperature of a column of air can be shown on a graph. If we could take a sample of air from some place in the column and insert it some place else, it would rise if it were warmer than its surroundings, stay where it was placed if the temperature were the same, and sink if it were cooler.

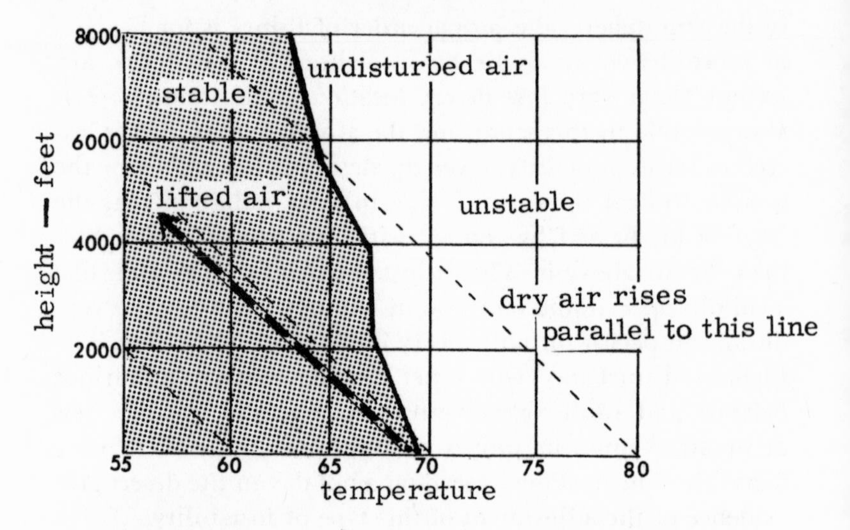

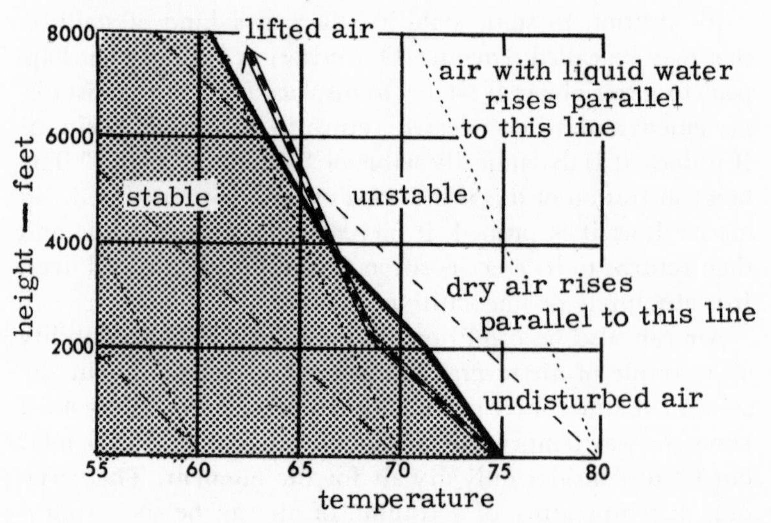

Stability of Lifted Air

Thus, the line on the graph that represents the actual temperatures in a column of air divides the graph into two areas: stable on the left, or colder, side and unstable on the right, or warmer, side.

But nature does not go about picking up a sample of air and inserting it elsewhere. One thing she does do, however, is lift air in connection with a front. The warm air moves upward over the frontal surface, and this is equivalent to picking up a sample of air. Repeatedly, the cooling of air as it moves upward has been mentioned. Now, if this discussion is to continue, we must give a numerical value to this cooling effect. Air in which condensation of water vapor does not take place—air which remains cloudless—cools 5.5°F for every 1,000 feet it is raised. On our graph, then, a family of lines can be drawn showing the rate of cooling of air as long as condensation does not take place.

Suppose the bottom of the column of air illustrated on the graph is lifted. Its temperature will change in accordance with the family of lines that has been drawn to show the rate of cooling. As long as this sample of air does not form clouds, it will be colder than its surroundings and will always fall back if it is no longer lifted. It is stable. But suppose clouds do form? Ah, that is another story. Saturated air cools less than dry air when it is raised. It drops in temperature only 2–3°F per 1,000 feet.

Let us now raise a sample of moist air from the bottom of the column. For the first few thousand feet, it remains unsaturated and cools its prescribed 5.5°F for each thousand feet. Then, finally, it has cooled enough to become saturated, and from that point on, it cools more slowly. As it continues on its upward path, it may remain colder than its surroundings. It may, however, become warmer, and if it does, it continues on its merry way upward without any further pushing by us or the impetus of a frontal surface. In the illustration pictured, the sample of air is conditionally stable. It is stable as long as it is not shoved higher than 4,000 feet. It is unstable if it is forced higher than this level. It should be noted that on our graph, 2,500 feet is the condensation level, for it is at this altitude that the first droplets of clouds form. The base of the clouds will be there. The height of the clouds will depend upon how much instability there is and how much water vapor is available for condensation.

Upward motion is not only induced by a front; there are other means by which nature lifts air. In its passage over a mountain, air is lifted. In the illustration, if the mountain were 2,500 feet high, it would have a cloudy cap, and if the air, in its flow over the mountain, reached a height of 4,000 feet, it would generate a thunderstorm—an orographic cloud, or orographic thunderstorm, in technical parlance.

Heating at the surface can produce the same effect. Suppose the layer of air near the ground gets increasingly warmer during the day. The graph of temperature as a function of height would have to be redrawn continually to show the increase in temperature in the lower layers. Eventually, the change in temperature might approach that critical value of 5.5°F per 1,000 feet. If this happened, the air would have neutral stability, and any displaced sample would be equally at home anywhere in the layer. If the air were sufficiently moist as well, condensation and instability would result. The final outcome would be a thunderstorm.

On any hot summer morning in regions where the air is moist, a forecaster will compute how high the surface temperature must rise to touch off a thunderstorm. If it is reasonable that this temperature will be reached in the course of the day, the little box on the upper-left side of the front page of the newspaper will carry the words "chance of afternoon thunderstorms."

Anyone who has crossed the ocean by sea or air—indeed, anyone who has sailed even briefly out of sight of land—has noticed the results of this lifting by heating. The first landfall is not the sight of the actual land mass but rather the glimpse of the clouds hovering over the coast. From miles away, in an otherwise blue Pacific—blue water below and blue sky above—you can see the tiny atoll with its cloud beacon serving the navigator as a point of reference in plotting his course. Each tiny key south of mainland Florida is punctuated by its cloud dot on an otherwise placid day.

Any discussion of atmospheric stability and instability should probably not be concluded until a few words have been said about smog, that irritating and sometimes deadly by-product of thoughtless and selfish technological advance. Let people incinerate their autumn leaves when they threaten to clutter the suburban lawn, let factories belch forth their white, black, yellow, or grey smoke, ignoring traps and filters, let buses and trucks vent their acrid gasoline and diesel dragons' breath into an atmosphere with just the right stability structure and smog will result. If the atmosphere remains static for several days, a situation like that in Donora, Pennsylvania, could arise. During five days in October 1948, twenty persons died and hundreds were stricken in that Pennsylvania town lying in a relatively deep and narrow valley of the Monongahela River. Atmospheric pollutants were trapped by an unfortunate combination of topographic and atmospheric circumstances in the air over the town.

An inversion in temperature puts the lid over an entire region, forming a baffle that traps everything in a narrow zone between the surface and the bottom of the inversion. We have noted that the greater the decrease in temperature with height, the smaller is the stability of an atmospheric layer and the greater the ease with which a sample of air can move upward. Conversely, the smaller the temperature gradient, the greater is the stability and the greater the resistance to anything moving upward. Sometimes the temperature in a relatively narrow layer can even increase with height, and a condition of maximum stability is achieved. Such a layer, with its inverted temperature structure, is called an inversion.

Nothing moves through it. All pollutants are trapped below it.

The wind can destroy an inversion by mixing the air to produce a more normal temperature structure, and a frontal passage can lift it and break it up. But while the weather pattern remains static, the inversion with its accompanying smog remains intact, only rising and falling slightly in a day-night breathing exercise.

From the air, such a layer looks like a cloud bank resting on the ground. If the smog or haze is tenuous enough, a two-way mirror is formed. People on the ground have no difficulty seeing through it to an aircraft above. The people in the plane, however, look down on billions of little reflectors that shine the sun's rays back into their eyes. Various ludicrous and dangerous situations can develop when pilot and ground observer see entirely different phenomena.

I learned a lesson about that in a particularly frightening way. An aviator friend of mine offered to fly me from Washington, where I was stationed, to New York, where my parents lived. We were to use a small navy plane, and my friend did not have an "instrument card." That meant that he knew how to fly only if he could maintain visual contact with the ground. The weather forecaster on duty at the air station informed him that it would be "captain's weather"—good visibility, light winds, no clouds. The two-way mirror was doing its deceptive job. The presence of a haze layer was not suspected. For a flight using visual contact rules, a copilot is not necessary. My friend was the only flyer on the plane, and I was accorded the privilege of occupying the copilot's seat on the right side of the cockpit.

From the ground, everything may have looked fine with ceiling and visibility unlimited, but in the air, in the vicinity of Wilmington, Delaware; Philadelphia, Pennsylvania; and Camden, New Jersey, a smog-haze layer stretched for miles.

We lost contact with the ground and thereby also lost our way. Needless to say, I was of little assistance in my impromptu role as copilot, although I searched diligently for the race track or rail junction that the aeronautical charts said should be somewhere below us.

We spent an anxious fifty minutes getting outselves located and on course again toward New York. Once we were headed in the right direction, I spent an even more anxious half hour at the controls of the plane, holding it in straight and level flight while my friend "rested." There he sat in his pilot's seat, eyes closed, first with a brick-red, perspiring face and later looking greyish green. Alternately, I tried to rouse him and tried to figure out the vagaries of the radio's frequency control in order to call for help. Fortunately, he did manage to revive sufficiently to take the controls for an emergency landing after I beseeched, begged, implored, and yelled at him that we were over Floyd Bennett Air Station. The control tower sent an ambulance out on the runway to take my friend away, and a strange pilot came aboard to taxi the plane off the field. Later, the hospital reported that he had had a mild heart attack.

Obviously, his illness could not be attributed to the haze layer which had not been spotted from the ground. Also, our plane came to no grief because of the layer having escaped notice. The next day, however, another plane lost its way in the same soup and crashed into the Empire State Building with a loss of fourteen lives.

9

In a Fog

An interesting point can be developed as a corollary to the discussion of smog and haze. This involves the kinds of atmospheric factors that are of concern to meteorologists. They do not care about smog or haze for its own sake. Identification of the areas in which these obstructions to vision occur and the numerical value of the consequent reduction in visibility does not help the person who draws the weather maps. He can do just as competent a job without this information. When electronic computers are used to prepare weather forecasts, data on visibility are not fed into the avid maws of the data processors.

Essentially, meteorology is a consumer service. The information it supplies is for the benefit of the activities in need of the information. Only a small part of the data is collected to meet strictly meteorological requirements—that is, data whose only usefulness is the production of a better weather map or a more detailed and accurate forecast.

In general, neither the meteorologist nor the consumer has been very clear-eyed about this distinction, much to the detriment of both. Two things happen as a result. First, inadequate attention, measured in research time and money, equipment development, and equipment procurement, is given to direct improvement of the science of meteorology. We pride ourselves on being a nation of practical people. We want value for our money, but we do not always know what really is of greater value. Given a choice between equipping every airfield with an automatic ceiling and visibility measuring device or providing meteorologists with more accurate and reliable means of measuring pressure and humidity aloft, which do we choose? The answer is obvious: that which does the greatest good to the greatest number. With increasing air travel by John Q. Public and with his convenience and safety very important to us, it must be better to put our money into the airfield device.

I cannot quarrel too much with this orientation. I, too, am interested in the flight safety of John Q. Public, not only in the abstract but also personally. I manage to spend a rather considerable number of hours in the air each year. Yet, a short-range view of aircraft safety can be self-defeating. Time was when the pace was slower and a pilot had time to digest the various bits and pieces of data fed him, permitting him to make the required adjustment. Time was when a plane, making its final approach and finding conditions not quite suitable, could "rev up" and come around again for another try at a landing. Then, the gadgetry measuring parameters such as visibility and ceiling were most valuable. Now, with supersonic aircraft, there is an ever decreasing possibility of buying a second chance. A jet aircraft commits itself to a landing early, and no matter what happens it must come down—in one or several pieces. The time is rapidly approaching when a plane commits itself to landing at Dulles National Airport even as its wheels leave the ground at O'Hare.

What is required to meet this type of aircraft-consumer requirement is not a measurement but a forecast—an accurate forecast that will be valid ten or fifteen minutes after the time it is made. With high-performance aircraft, it is no longer good enough to say what average conditions or even present conditions are, no matter how well-defined. With small variations becoming more and more crucial, reliance on persistence of present values becomes less valuable.

To provide real help to the aircraft industry, meteorologists must make the kind of advances that will permit them to prepare this and other kinds of specific forecasts. If these advances can only be made by permitting the meteorologist to make measurements of direct benefit to him alone, it is shortsighted to withhold the means of accomplishment from him.

I cannot make a case proving that better meteorological measurements will solve the aircraft-landing problem, but I can plead for better measurements, which will lead ultimately to meeting other requirements of high-flying transonic aircraft. The nature, cause, and predictability of clear-air turbulence bears more investigation. A number of planes have disintegrated in the air, presumably due to this phenomenon. There have been a number of limited investigations of why certain patches of clear air are thunderstorm-rough, but the fundamentals have been neglected and only the superficial features examined. The research into this phenomenon did not start back far enough, principally because of the lack of necessary data.

My complaint is neither peculiar to me nor to meteorology. It is the theme song of all scientists who view with dismay (adopting a useful phrase) the current trend to exploit every technological advantage to the point of diminishing returns, calling it progress, while sufficient thought is not given to the development of new theories and principles that will form the bases for different lines of technological developments.

A second consequence of the short-range, consumer-oriented point of view is that occasionally the wrong element is measured—one of no use whatever either to supplier or consumer. The measurement of refractive index provides a good illustration. In Chapter 7, the bending of radar waves was discussed and the statement was made that the amount of bending depended upon the temperature and humidity structure of the lower atmosphere. Refractive index can be computed from these factors together with a small pressure correction. Thus, for the determination of radar performance, whether the radar is airborne or ground based, refractive index is important. There is a special instrument that measures refractive index, a refractometer. What could be more logical than to equip operational aircraft with refractometers so that they can measure refractive index as they go along? In addition, research or weather planes outfitted with refractometers can be sent spiraling upward and downward through the atmosphere to measure refractive index in a column of air.

And indeed, this was done. Unfortunately, in so far as the operational aircraft were concerned, the value of the refractive index at the plane's location has no significance for a radar beam that travels for miles and miles in parts of the atmosphere where the plane is not flying. As for the spiraling aircraft sampling the atmosphere, the data they obtain are certainly useful for radar beams traversing that sample of air at that time. Unfortunately, no one knows how refractive index changes with time and space. Thus, no projection or forecast of changes can be made. How pressure, temperature, and humidity change is known fairly well, and, if instead of refractive index, the aircraft measured these parameters, much more value could be derived from the data obtained.

Parenthetically, it should be noted that probably the single, most vital meteorological need is for a simple, rapid, accurate way of measuring the humidity of air. The methods now in use satisfy none of these requirements. In general, one of four procedures is used. The time-honored way involves stretching fine, unbleached, unpermanented blond human hair between two posts. With changes in humidity, the hair stretches or shrinks so that a pen arm fastened to one of the posts moves as the tension changes. At one time during the war, the Navy had a file drawer full of letters from patriotic citizens offering hair for meteorological use. Oddly enough, it was usually someone else's tresses that were to be sacrificed: "my wife's," "my daughter's," and so on. Currently, substances other than hair are used in the same way. Goldbeater's skin, which is the membrane of the large intestine of an ox, is prominent among these.

A second method for measuring humidity involves using substances for which electric resistance changes as they absorb or lose water vapor. What makes this otherwise convenient method undesirable is the length of time it takes for equilibrium to be established between water vapor in the atmosphere and absorption on a surface.

Since the evaporation of liquid water is accompanied by a reduction in temperature, a psychrometer, a combination of wet and dry thermometers, can also be used. The bulb of one thermometer is moistened while the other is dry. The two are whirled through the air together and then read. The dry bulb reads air temperature, while, if any water evaporated from the wet bulb, the mercury in that thermometer tube gives a lower temperature reading. From the difference in temperature, the amount of evaporation can be deduced and therefore the degree of unsaturation of the surrounding air. For temperatures below freezing, the ice-water relationship causes problems and, in any case, the method is not very satisfactory for other than routine ground station use.

The most sophisticated method uses a photoelectric eye that peers at a tiny mirror. As long as the mirror reflects a beam of light, its temperature is gradually reduced. Eventually, the air touching the mirror must deposit its moisture content on the cold surface because the dewpoint is reached. The photoelectric eye senses this obstruction to bright reflectivity and turns off the cooling system until it sees clearly again. The temperature of the mirror is measured, of course. In addition to the obvious complications of this rather elaborate system, there is the basic problem that in a temperature region just below the freezing point of water, one cannot guarantee that it is the dewpoint that is measured. It could just as easily be the frost point.

Does anyone have a break-through in humidity measurement, please?

By and large, humidity is needed by meteorologists and not directly by the consumer. Those who need weather information for their activities use derivatives from humidity. Part of an icing forecast for aircraft is based on humidity and the greater part of the forecast of that airway demon, fog, is obviously based on the moisture content of the air.

Fog. Many people are interested in fog. Almost everyone is prepared to define it as a cloud resting on the ground, all but dismissing any further discussion by the flat factuality of this statement. To be sure, both fog and clouds are composed of tiny droplets of liquid water suspended in air. To that extent the definition is accurate, but the implicit assumption that a cloud can form at any altitude and therefore be so close to the ground as to be fog is somewhat misleading.

If we consider radiation fog again and realize that it is formed by cooling of the ground during a clear night, cooling sufficient to produce condensation in the lowest layers of the atmosphere, it is apparent that the matter of fog cannot be shoved aside just by saying "cloud on the ground." It is produced differently and persists under different conditions. In a dead calm, the radiation fog is only inches thick because it is truly only the layer next to the ground that gets cooled—

apparently legless people are seen wandering about. With a light wind, there is enough mixing so that a greater volume of air gets cooled. The fog builds up and can become quite deep as well as dense—at any distance, people disappear altogether. With a stronger wind, the mixing is even more pronounced—so much that no sample of air gets cooled to condensation. No fog.

Certainly, all fogs are not produced by radiation cooling. There are other ways by which a volume of air can be cooled to the condensation point. Residents of both New England and West Coast regions should be well aware of another type of fog formation: advection fog. Instead of a mass of moist air being cooled in place, it is moved or "advected" to another location where it may be cooled. Consider the northeastern coast of the North American continent, for example. Close to land, traveling southward, is the Labrador oceanic current, icy cold, as any intrepid bather can testify, fresh off the polar ice cap. Farther out to sea, a broad, slow-moving, meandering river stretches from the tropical Atlantic to Northern Europe, there to give its blessing of temperate climate to geographic regions whose high latitudes should otherwise suffer Arctic cold; it is the Gulf Stream. Over this river imbedded in the ocean, the air becomes warm and moist. If the wind blows toward shore, however, the balmy, moisture-laden air is carried over the Labrador Current. Fog—advection fog—results.

The West Coast experiences the same phenomenon. The Pacific immediately offshore is also cold, due in part to the Japanese Current, which circles from Japan, around the Aleutian Islands, past Alaska and northwestern Canada, and in part because of "upwelling," the overturning of water that occurs along the west coast of all continents, by which cold bottom water is brought to the surface. A wind from the west brings warm Pacific air from far out over the cold coastal waters. The air gets cooled. The moisture gets condensed—more advection fog.

Interestingly enough, a light and rather insignificant fog can also be produced by exactly the reverse atmospheric situation. Advection fog occurs when warm air travels over a cold surface. Steam fog happens when cold air travels over a warm, moist surface. This usually takes place in late fall when lakes and rivers still retain much of their summer heat while the air is rapidly achieving winter temperatures. The warm water evaporates its vapor into the cold air, where it condenses. It is a double pleasure that these misty spectral fingers probing into the air, which so reward the early-morning stroller along a river or canal path, cause no bother to anyone.

A related phenomenon, which gives no pleasure and much trouble, is produced by the opposite situation—the topsy-turvy world with the stream of water above and the cold air below. Above a frontal surface, the warm air produces a vertical stream: a flow of rain resulting from the upward movement. The rain, falling through the cold air below the frontal surface, may not reach the ground. It may merely saturate that lower layer of air, producing a fog. The area from the surface of the earth to the frontal surface can be filled by a thick, white "soup," and if the front is one of the gradually sloping warm variety, it can blanket thousands of square miles in its cottony veil.

At one time, I was deeply involved with fog in connection with my work: its dissipation on the one hand and the measurement of how much it obstructed visibility on the other. The Navy had a Landing Aids Experimental Air Station located at Arcata, California, where advection fog was very frequent. All sorts of wonderful experiments were carried out there and methods developed to assist pilots in making landings under conditions of reduced visibility. The work at Arcata was guided by a steering committee composed of personnel from the Washington bureaus as well as experimenters from California. My boss appointed me to the committee to represent our office.

The greatest success was achieved in directly helping the pilot to make his landings under adverse conditions, although many experiments were also performed in an effort to remove or reduce the fog. New types of intense lights were constructed in the approach zone, arranged in such a way that they formed a distinctive pattern when the pilot was on the proper glide path for a landing. These lights would also show up in other recognizable patterns if he were flying too high or low, too far to the right or left. Derivatives of these researches can be seen on the outskirts of any major airport, marking the approach to the all-weather runways.

Then there was the ILS, Instrument Landing System, in which an electronically controlled pair of needles mounted on the instrument panel in the cockpit directly in front of the pilot hovered at right angles to each other, making a large plus sign when the pilot was gliding properly toward the end of the runway. Any deviation from the glide path would send the needles akimbo. This system is also in general use today.

Finally, and to me more interesting, was GCA, Ground Control Approach, by which radar operators sitting in trailer trucks just off the center of the runway, talked the planes down. One radar swept horizontally in a small arc while another swept vertically, also in a small arc. If the plane were on course, it could be seen in the center of each of the scopes. Markings on the scopes showed how much the plane was off course. The master radar controlman would say "You are fifty feet above the glide path. Come down a little. You're doing fine. You are now seventy-five feet above. Come on down some more. You're doing fine. You are right on. That's just fine. Come right two degrees. That's good. Just a little more right. That's fine. If you look out now you should be able to see the end of the runway. You're on your own."

"That's fine! That's good!" was as important to GCA as the radar. The quality of the voice the pilots heard in their earphones was critical. Regardless of competency, one voice encouraged the pilot to "give over" his controls to a man on the ground while another inspired no confidence whatsoever.

As a member of the steering committee, although all this was outside of my purview, I rode light planes, heavy planes, DC-3's and -4's, B-25's, and B-17's in countless approaches to see how these systems operated. I made a few breath-taking landings illegally ensconced in the nose bubble of a B-17, from which vantage point nothing of the airplane can be seen except, overhead, the floor of the cockpit. When I came down for a landing sitting there, I just saw the concrete runway coming up closer and closer. I kept wondering whether the wheels were down. Just at the last moment, when I was certain that the plastic bubble I was sitting in was going to make the initial contact between plane and ground, I realized that the plane was rolling along on its wheels and I had survived to make another take-off. Why Air Force safety regulations required that the nose-bubble position remain vacant except while the plane was fully airborne is no mystery to me.

Has it been noted that all these flights were made in sparkling, clear weather? They were. Nothing cleared away fog as effectively as the arrival of the steering committee. During a whole series of semimonthly visits, we never encountered the least obstruction to vision. Statistically, seventeen days of fog might prevail during the month of one of our visits; actually it might have been zero ceiling, zero visibility on the day before we came and again the day after we left, but no matter how long we stayed waiting for it to happen, it always eluded us.

This state of affairs was high-lighted by an almost tragic,

but fortunately only ludicrous, event attending one of my visits to the West Coast. I arrived at San Francisco on a Saturday morning and found one of the Arcata planes waiting for me at the airport to ferry me north.

"Are they working over the week end?" I asked in bewilderment, for such had not been the plans.

"No. Most of the committee will come Monday," was the answer. "We'll send a big plane to pick them up then."

"Well, thanks for the special service, fellows," I said, "but, if you don't mind, I'll spend the week end in San Francisco and fly up on Monday with the others."

The pilot of the light plane agreed that I was choosing wisely and went to the operations office to get a clearance for his flight back to Arcata, but Arcata was completely fogged in.

"Think nothing of it," the pilot volunteered. "They'll turn on their antifog devices. We fly into that stuff all the time."

Obviously, officialdom could not accept such a statement. The airfield at Arcata was closed, and no flight could be cleared to land there. Regulations said so. The plane could fly to Eureka, however.

The pilot, knowing both the terrain and the weather situation, was appalled. A cliff, or palisade, separates Eureka and Arcata, with Arcata sitting on top and Eureka below on the coast. Arcata was socked in because the wind was blowing from the ocean bringing in the layer of moisture-laden air. Eureka's field was open because it was below the fog layer. But because of Eureka's location at the base of a cliff, any plane always has to come in from the ocean to make a landing. With the wind from the sea, this would mean a downwind landing and the runway, short at best, would seem even shorter without the braking effect of a headwind.

All the pilot's arguments went for naught, however, and he was finally forced to accept the clearance for Eureka.

When he made his landing there, the runway did turn out to be too short. The plane wound up sitting on its nose off the end of the runway. Fortunately, no one was injured, and the plane suffered only the minor damage of bent propellors.

I did not know anything about this until Monday, of course, when we took off in crystal-clear weather for Arcata with the complete approbation of the operations officer in San Francisco.

In addition to the use of committee meetings, other systems of fog dispersal were tested at Arcata, and a great number of the most detailed measurements of the size, number, and electric charge of the fog droplets was made. Two of the fog-dispersal methods were extremely interesting. One of these was based on the nature of a standing sound wave with nodes and antinodes. The idea was to have the sound move the individual fog droplets to the nodal positions where, due to crowding, they would collide one with the other to form large drops. These would then fall out under the influence of gravity. A number of very high-powered sirens were assembled to provide the necessary sound energy. All that happened, however, was that half of the state of California received an unscheduled air-raid alert. The fog remain untouched.

One method of fog dispersal did work, however. It was imported from Great Britain where it had been used to deal rather effectively with the radiation fog they have there. In keeping with the usual predilection for alphabetese, it was called Fog Intensity, Dispersal Of—a most un-English construction of English words. The initials make the word FIDO, however, which is a most satisfactory term.

FIDO involves lining the entire length of the airplane runway with pipes and burners. With the approach of an aircraft, the flow of gasoline is started, and the burners are ignited. In a moment, several thousands of feet of runway are bordered on both sides by roaring, but controlled, flames. The heat both lifts the fog, leaving a cleared rectangle immediately over the runway, and evaporates some of the water. As a side effect, the glow of the flames can be seen from miles away over the fog bank and serves to guide the plane in.

Except for the very understandable reluctance to mix fire and aircraft—a slight mishap involving either in a landing procedure could have disastrous consequences—FIDO worked very well indeed for a limited range of wind velocities. If the wind was too low, combustion products polluted the air, decreasing the visibility. If it was too high, the heating requirements rose most uneconomically; and worse yet, the clearing took place downwind rather than over the runway.

Tremendous advances were made at Arcada in the FIDO system. Electrically controlled firing at a remote location was substituted for men running with torches down the runway, and, by using a method of preheating the fuel, inexpensive diesel oil was satisfactorily used in lieu of the expensive aviation gasoline of the earlier installations. The cost per aircraft landing was brought down from hundreds of dollars to something less than fifty dollars.

Many other attempts were made to dissipate fog. Chemicals—the usual dessicants employed in home and factory for drying—were dumped from airplanes or dispersed by blowers on the ground. Farmers and plane handlers alike complained of contamination and corrosion. Charged wires were strung, or charged sand thrown into the air. Various citizens, through caution lest their ideas be stolen, or through cupidity, thinking to make a fast buck by selling stock in a manufacturing company, offered "black boxes" for the test station to try.

It would not be entirely truthful to call the results flatly negative in all cases. Occasionally, clearing did occur, but it was never possible to prove that the technique employed produced the change. By its nature, fog is a sometime thing, spotty and unpredictable. If a hole appeared in the fog, as it sometimes did, it occurred just as frequently upwind of the experimental area with black boxes or the charged wires. And how could that be explained? In effect, the results were negative.

A vitally significant lesson can be, but has not been, learned from this. Simply stated, the lesson is that before you know that you have affected a situation, you must know what would have happened if you had not done anything but watch. Unless the results of the efforts are truly dramatic, widespread, and instantaneous, there must be a standard or norm to measure results against. These were not available for fog-dispersal testing. Unfortunately, many unknowns still continue to plague meteorologists with respect to fog. We do not really know how to measure its intensity, for example, and this is a vitally needed piece of information.

Let us consider how we measure visibility and how data on visibility is used. The usual method involves standing at the center of a well-mapped area. The observer notes that the steeple of St. Andrew's Church is visible but that the antenna of the local radio station just beyond it cannot be seen. The map indicates that St. Andrew's is one-half mile away, while the antenna is three-quarters of a mile distant. Within narrow limits, visual range has been measured. Of course a somewhat uncertain quantity has been measured, since presumably the church and the tall tower are not exactly in a line and the visibility need not be the same in all directions. To determine visual range this exercise can, of course, be repeated in several directions and an average taken; or perhaps just the lowest value obtained can be used, because it represents the worst possible condition. Needless to say, the convention of reporting visibility has long since been established, but the usefulness of the reported value to the consumer can well be questioned.

The aircraft pilot is, of course, the individual most directly concerned. With proper training, he can fly indefinitely without seeing the ground. Electronic navigational aids abound to help him travel from one place to another without using visual landmarks. Only when he lands must he be able to see—see the end of the runway—and he must be able to find that point from no less a distance than a mile and a height of a hundred or more feet (depending upon the type of plane he is flying). He comes down to earth following a slanting course, called his glide path. On it there is a critical point which, when passed, means that he is pretty well committed to a landing.

What the pilot needs, then, is a slant visibility along his glide path which tells him if he will be able to see at and beyond this critical point in his descent. What he gets from the control tower is a combination of horizontal visibility measured by looking at St. Andrew's and a vertical visibility determined by the height of the bases of the lowest layer of clouds. It is quite apparent that he does not get what he needs and that the two measurements he is given can be quite misleading.

At sea, the problem of determining visibility is more difficult but usually less critical. Did I say more difficult? Impossible would be more correct. There are no fixed points over an ocean. An accompanying ship may or may not be in visual range, but unless two ships maneuver to find the limiting distance at which they can just see each other, there is no way of knowing what the visibility is. On the other hand, the same absence of fixed points for measurements serves to make aircraft operations at sea safer, since slant visibility is not really required. Without buildings and terrain to clear, the plane can make a low-level approach. As long as the ceiling is a couple of hundred feet high, it can descend to clear air below the cloud deck at a considerable distance from the carrier and make a satisfactory visual approach. If the horizontal visibility in the lower layers is reduced, however, the flying problem at sea is just as difficult as on land.

Considerable effort has been expended in trying to lick the problem of measuring visibility: horizontal, or slant, or both. For a while, I thought I had found a possible answer. As happens so often, it was a by-product of research aimed at another goal. As in the case of radar development for weather purposes, it looked as though what was another person's poison might turn out to be our meat.

Shipboard communicators were struggling with maintaining communications between ships and between ships and aircraft without, at the same time, giving away their positions to the enemy. Radio direction finding was well enough advanced that the location of a radio transmitter could be pinpointed. Thus, often, radio silence was mandatory. Certainly the use of visible light signals—Morse code transmission by using a shutter over a searchlight at night—was out in a war in which the first line of defense was black-out discipline. But infrared communications—there was a real potential.

Take the limited but vital problem of IFF—Identification: Friend or Foe. Is an approaching airplane or a distant ship hostile? Particularly at night, when its configuration cannot be seen for recognition, how can this be determined without exchanging passwords or radio identification? It would be wonderful if invisible light could serve the same purpose. Several possible ways seemed worth exploring. An inert, or passive, recognition system seemed feasible in which both visual and radio silence could be preserved but where an infrared beam could shine on suitable reflector beads. Friendly ships and aircraft could carry an array of such reflectors, and the reflected radiation could be picked up by equipment similar to the snooperscope, or sniperscope, used by the infantryman for seeing in the dark. All friends would give a "good" infrared signal. Enemies would not.

It also seemed possible that a more direct method would be useful. Each type of ship must have its own typical radiation pattern depending upon its construction design. Every object emits infrared radiation, the quality depending upon its temperature. Thus, the boiler-room area of a ship should show up as the hottest part, emitting the most intense infrared rays. Other parts of a ship must give off radiation proportionate to the equilibrium temperatures they can maintain with respect to their surroundings. Presumably, recognition training, if this system worked, could be geared to infrared patterns as well as to the usual visual configuration.

In addition, by using an on-off device on an infrared beam, it might be possible to conduct coded conversations. At any rate, research was instituted to capitalize on some of these principles, but progress soon came to a grinding halt because of the uncertainty of one dominating and crippling factor—the influence of weather. Water is quite opaque to certain frequencies of infrared. Under low-visibility conditions, in mist, or drizzle, or fog, the infrared identification system did not work. When the visibility was poor, all that was detected was the weather.

The big question as far as my office was concerned was whether the decrease in intensity of the infrared beam could not be used to measure the thickness of the atmospheric obstructions. At many a conference table, we explored the various concepts inherent in the existing test equipment and developed a series of equipment adaptations and experiments to test our hypotheses. At last, the experimental equipment was ready and the testing schedule prepared. It was time to alert my boss that all was ready.

"Whom are you going to send to witness the tests?" I asked.

"It's your project. You, of course. Any reason why I shouldn't?"

"Yes." Reluctantly, I told him that the equipment had been installed on a PCE, a patrol craft escort, the smallest vessel the Navy still calls a ship rather than a boat, and that the tests could only be conducted at sea.

"Well?"

For the moment, I hated him. He knew as surely as I that it was illegal for a Wave to go to sea on any but a passenger vessel. He seemed to be rubbing my nose in the disappointing fact that I could not follow up on my own project. I pointed out my disqualification.

"Don't you want to go?" he asked. "If you do, I'd think that the two of us, together, could manage to confuse the Bureau of Naval Personnel sufficiently to get you a set of orders."

He did not have to repeat the suggestion, and he was, of course, completely correct that it was not difficult to throw the necessary smoke screen to get travel orders from "BuPers" without letting the processing clerks really know what they were doing. The equipment and project were classified, and deft use of the words "confidential" and "secret" served to camouflage the nature of the transaction.

In every other research project with which I have been involved, the work was always paramount, despite any unusual circumstances in which I might find myself. In this particular case, the importance of the project dimmed to insignificance when measured against my personal adventures.

Careful preliminary arrangements had to be made involving not only the infrared equipment and the test procedures but also my status with the test program. The latter was a matter of meeting two sets of requirements: getting the ship prepared for me to go to sea with it and getting me prepared for the ship.

A telephone call to the captain of the PCE, which used Lewes, Delaware, as home port, took care of alerting the ship adequately. Took care of it, that is, once said captain recovered from shock, hilarity, and amazement, in that order. His final reaction showed eagerness and anticipation. I could have his cabin, he decided instantly, since it was the only one with sufficient privacy: a door rather than a curtain separating it from the companionway and a private head (bathroom to the nonnautical). He would bunk with his executive officer.

My personal preparations became more frenzied after the phone call. Although I had a piece of paper declaring me an officer and a gentleman in the United States Navy, I was strictly a landlubber type. My knowledge of shipboard procedures was just sufficient to suggest that there was a long and involved ritual of stock phrases and mandatory salutes to be exchanged when you boarded a commissioned naval vessel. I buried myself in the *Naval Reserve Officer's Guide* to learn the ritual. My associates in the office combined cramming my head full of useless details with pulling my leg unmercifully. They were rather less than helpful. That I outranked the captain of the ship, who held that title because he was a commanding officer, had become apparent during the course of our telephone conversation. As a "senior" officer, I just could not fall on my face and disgrace myself, the Waves, and all womankind.

You request permission to come aboard as you go up the gangway. When this is granted, you turn aft and salute the ensign—the United States flag—and then salute the officer of the deck, who may well be an ensign too, the two-legged variety. He returns both salutes. In the wardroom, it is not proper to . . . . It is proper to . . . . A long list of taboos and musts follows.

As I walked down the dock at Lewes, I was still drilling myself on the fundamentals of naval etiquette. As a matter of fact, I was so immersed in this exercise that I failed to be impressed by the carefully correct attire—blue uniform, including grey gloves and binoculars—of the officer of the deck. The *Naval Reserve Officer's Guide* had alerted me to expect this. How was I to know that on a small ship like a PCE, normally only an admiral's inspection was sufficient incentive for protocol and dress-up. Afterwards, my hosts confessed to disappointment that I had failed to be impressed with the great honor accorded me.

It is impossible for me to report whether I saluted in proper order and repeated the correct formulas. As I went up the gangplank, all I was aware of was the blare of the loudspeaker. "Now hear this!" it announced. "Wave officer aboard. Observe all proper precautions."

We sailed immediately, and as soon as we had left the shelter of Delaware Bay and were out in the Atlantic, we sat down to dinner—eight of us: the captain, five of his officers, a civilian engineer who came with the equipment, and I. The executive officer was on the bridge. Although the steak had been so overdone and tough that it should have taken several minutes to masticate each mouthful sufficiently to get it down, the hash-brown potatoes were so loaded with grease that the process of swallowing was greatly simplified. With a minimum of effort, food slid down, which was just as well since the taste buds were not anxious to be involved in the alimentary process.

The officers were quite profuse in their apologies for the food—apologizing not only for the current meal but for all future ones as well. They had lost their cook (appendicitis) and had drafted a seaman as replacement. Steak and potatoes were all he knew how to cook, a diet as rough on the officers' pocketbooks as on their digestion.

Realizing that I would never impress them with my nautical skills, I decided I would try my culinary ones on them. For the rest of the trip, I prepared the main meal for the wardroom, and, as ranking officer aboard, undoubtedly made a kind of history that will never be recorded in any navy document.

Our equipment could be operated only at night, so the working day started after dinner and lasted until dawn. This was rather inconvenient since the ship's crew worked largely during daylight hours. The inconvenience was suffered by all hands; all but the scope of the infrared equipment was set up just aft of the crew's quarters below decks, and a dozen times during the night we would have to make some adjustment or other. The lights would be switched on in the sleeping compartment. Someone would shout "Coming through. Cover up." We would make the necessary changes, switch off the lights, and go back to watching the display assembly set up on the bridge. On the other hand, we would sleep during the day, having had breakfast before retiring, while the crew chipped paint or occupied themselves with other noisy tasks about the ship. I am certain that paint was never better chipped than just outside the bulkhead of the captain's cabin where I presumably slept. I wondered at times whether the chipping process ever penetrated clear through the hull of a ship.

We would travel up and down the coast line looking for good sources of infrared radiation, anchor, make both infrared readings and visual range estimates, using radar to check distances. Then we would pull up anchor, find a new location, and repeat the process. The March weather was most cooperative. Although it was cold—the penetrating cold of the North Atlantic in late winter—we had the gamut from sparkling clear to heavy fog to work with.

The captain, watch officer, civilian engineer, and I huddled behind a windscreen on the open bridge drinking coffee. Below us, the anchor detail spent the night alternately letting the anchor down and pulling it up again. It must have been nasty, wet work. Early in the evening, their language, which came through loud and clear to us on the bridge, was quite moderate considering their labors. An occasional "hell" or "damn" was used for seasoning. The captain would apologize for the profanity and remind me that I knew what men were like. As the hours wore on, these expletives became more frequent and were joined by more resounding Anglo-Saxon words together with all their possible derivatives: verbs, adjectives, and nouns coming from the same few four-letter roots. These the captain did not hear although the next "hell" or "damn" would be accorded a better-than-average apology.

The results we were getting from our test program were rather better than we had expected, although they were by no means startling. It was obvious that considerably more development would be required to get anything like an operational piece of equipment. On the third night of tests, the experimental program came to an abrupt end. We had made one adjustment too many on the equipment. The crew reported a fire in the aft compartment. Our equipment burned insulation for a few minutes and then stood there, a worthless pile of junk. When the emergency was declared over, we all turned in to our bunks, rather gratefully resuming the daily routine of normal human beings.

With the test program perforce finished, it was time for me to return to Washington. In a fog so thick that the jack staff on the stern could not be seen from the bridge, we proceeded slowly up Delaware Bay under radar control. But the captain could not return to the dock without greater visibility. Since the forecast received by radio gave no promise that the fog would lift in the immediate future, we decided that I should go ashore in the whaleboat.

A few minutes later, I presented myself on the top deck clad in my skirted Navy uniform (I had worn borrowed foul-weather clothing all the rest of the time) to watch the readying of the whaleboat. Provisions, water, preservers, and signaling gear were all checked, as though for a long voyage, and then, finally, the boat was swung out on its davits and lowered. Only when it made its initial contact with the briny water did it suddenly occur to me that I was still on the ship and that there were several miles (or so it seemed) of distance between us. How this space was to be spanned was not long left in doubt. A rope ladder was thrown over the side.

"Shall I go down?" I asked, realizing that the microscopic quantity of courage I possessed would never be more flourishing.

"No, let me go first."

This idea became more acceptable to me as I watched carefully how the captain placed his hands and feet on the insubstantial rope lattice as he descended.

"Now?" I called down throwing a leg over the side.

"No, wait." The captain stood in earnest conversation with the whaleboat crew, which had descended with the boat.

"Now," he said finally, and, somehow, a few minutes later, I was in the whaleboat. "Sorry to keep you waiting," he told me. "I had to impress on the men that the first one who looked up as you came down would get punished at Captain's Mast."

Infrared visibility measurements? The equipment was never replaced. The results of the first tests had not been sufficiently clear-cut to win any enthusiasm in the Washington offices, and other projects, considered more important, could benefit from the input of diverted money.

10

Weather on the Air

Enough about purely local measurements and about personal adventures. The single most exciting feature about weather is perhaps that it is almost global in scope. Actually, it is only semiglobal since, except for long-range effects and for a narrow band near the equator, the northern and southern hemispheres have little to do with each other. But a whole hemisphere of interdependence is still something to wonder at.

Not only do clouds and storms cross national boundaries without passport or visas, but also every forecaster is dependent on meteorological measurements made everywhere else. Ideologies play no part in the work aspects of meteorologists and their data. The juxtaposition of international conflicts and weather cooperation can be quite startling. Before leaving for work, you read your morning newspaper crammed with tales of tension between this country and others. You get to your office and glance at the northern-hemisphere chart. Except when there is overt war, the conflicts are not apparent on the weather map. All the information is there just as it always is.

During a period when East-West relationships were most strained and TV newscasters alternately depressed and wryly amused their viewers with farcical scenes from turbulent meetings at the United Nations, unpublicized, businesslike, worth-while conferences were being conducted by other representatives of these same countries. The member nations of the World Meteorological Organization, one of the subdivisions of the United Nations, were working successfully at establishing common meteorological codes, definitions, and standards.

It is difficult for an outsider to realize how great the international cooperation in weather really is. In other scientific fields there are also exchanges, but these are more guarded. Individuals from both sides of the Iron Curtain get together not so much, perhaps, to exchange information as to learn. They want to guarantee that their side will not fall behind in the struggle for scientific prowess. Scientists in Western laboratories are curious about what is going on in the Eastern counterparts, but they are not dependent upon the results achieved there, and vice versa. With meteorology, it is different. For much of the work, although not all, there is mutual dependence. Long-range (time) and global (area) forecasts cannot be made without all the data. The voracious maws of the electronic computer swallow every scrap of information and remain unsatisfied. And the Russians and Americans (as well as the Swedes, British, and others) have electronic computers to help forecast weather.

Enlightened self-interest can produce strange assemblages. For many years, I raged at what I considered the neglect of the publicity value of these productive get togethers. The general populace should know, I felt, that in this world of strife, cooperation did exist in certain areas. My pleas for good news releases were largely ignored. In recent years, I have come to believe that the soft pedaling was well-advised. Too much publicity might have forced narrow nationalism in meteorological congresses where internationalism was implicit.

The lack of knowledge of international cooperation made dealings with the press difficult. Once, when the Navy had a press conference to show the first pictorial meteorological interchange by radio between a naval unit on the Antarctic continent and our office in Washington, the reporters almost ignored the tremendous achievement we were presenting. They devoted nearly all the allotted time to a cross examination designed to ferret out the degree of Russian-American weather interchange. We had been cautioned to speak only in general terms. The session became progressively more unsatisfactory as the reporters sensed withheld information and we, unskilled in press-conference techniques, were driven farther and farther into untenable corners.

Well, meteorology—the forecasting of weather—depends upon the interchange of weather data. Interchange starts on a purely local scale and expands. The United States is divided into fifteen major and fourteen supplementary regions for aviation-weather purposes, and each station in each region informs each other station at least once every hour of the weather that will affect aircraft operations. If the weather is changing rapidly, the messages are sent more frequently: indeed, each time there is a significant change in one of the weather factors. The data come in at 100 words per minute and no item is more than 60 minutes old.

The heart of this system is the teletypewriter. In each weather office, one or more of these automatic machines is clattering away at all times. Each sequence starts promptly at half past the hour. In one of the regions of which Washington, D. C., is a part, it starts with Buffalo, N. Y., covers all of western New York, Pennsylvania, eastern Ohio, parts of West Virginia and Virginia, and the coastal region between New York City and Baltimore, Maryland. In a distance of approximately two hundred miles between New York City and Washington, the following stations report:

MacArthur Field at Islip, Long Island, New York
John F. Kennedy International Airport, Long Island, New York
Bendix Airport, Teterboro, New Jersey
Newark Airport, New Jersey
LaGuardia Airport, New York City
Westchester County Airport, White Plains, New York
North Philadelphia Airport, Pennsylvania
Philadelphia International Airport, Pennsylvania
Friendship Airport near Baltimore, Maryland
Washington National Airport, Washington, D.C.
Dulles International Airport, Chantilly, Virginia

Once the immediate area of interest is covered, more remote data are relayed. Before the hour is over, the complete eastern half of the United States is covered and a forecaster in Washington can draw a detailed hourly map of that half of the country.

The data given are for aviation use. A typical message might be:

ORF 25⦶E7ØØ⦷1ØØØ⊕5R–GF Ø95/72/7Ø/18Ø9/98Ø

To the weatherman, this messages contributes the following information about weather at Norfolk, Virginia. There are scattered clouds at 2,500 feet. Norfolk estimates the height of a broken cloud deck at 7,000 feet (E7ØØ⦷) and of an overcast (⊕) at 10,000 feet. The visibility is 5 miles in light rain (R–) and ground fog (GF). The atmospheric pressure is 1,009.5 millibars while the temperature is 72°F. If the temperature were reduced to 70°, the dewpoint would be reached. The wind is from the south (180°) and is blowing at 9 miles per hour. If pilots crank the value 29.80 into their altimeters, their instruments will read the height of the Norfolk airport above mean sea level when their planes are sitting on the runway.

On his airways chart, the meteorologist finds the little circle representing Norfolk and enters this information around it.

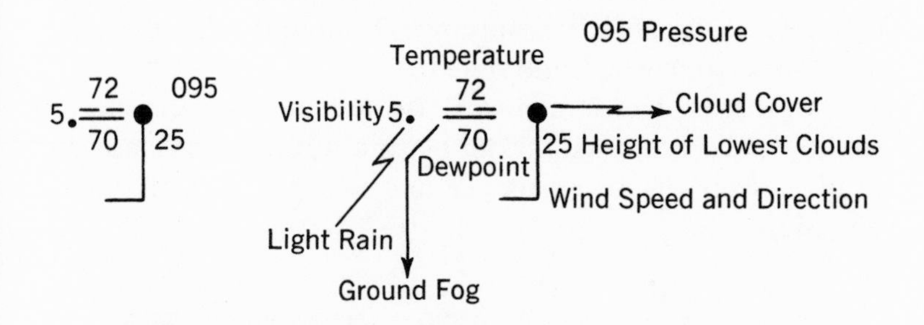

To supplement this information, pilots in flight radio in their observations if they consider them noteworthy. Mainly, this would be occasioned by their encountering conditions that were not treated conclusively in their flight forecasts. These reports are called pilot reports, or PIREPS, and are coded and put on the teletype circuit for all to read. For example, if at 8:45 Central Standard Time, the pilot of a C-54 in radio contact with Bismarck, North Dakota, reports that he is encountering an 82-knot wind from an easterly (080°) direction and that he is flying 30 miles west of Bismarck at an altitude of 6,000 feet above mean sea level, the weathermen at Bismarck Airport would get busy. Five minutes later, or at 1450 hours, Greenwich time, this message would clatter out on all the teletypes in the Bismarck region:

BIS PIREP 1450Z 30 W BIS 0845C WND 080 82KT 60.

If a B-58 flying over Navasota, Texas (airway symbol AVS), at 6:13 Central Standard Time reports to Houston that the top of the overcast is 8,500 feet above mean sea level, Houston would enter the data for all to read. If the message were sent at 1218 Greenwich time, the PIREP would read:

HOU PIREP 1218Z OVR AVS 0613C O 85

In addition to these airways messages, once each six hours stations all over the world simultaneously take a complete set of surface observations. They code the data into a World Meteorological Organization approved form and relay the message to everyone who is interested.

A wealth of data is included. Because it is fascinating to see how much information can be transmitted in a relatively short message, let us reproduce one together with its interpretation.

I	II	III	IV	V	VI	VII
70055	83604	81022	08001	15608	60319	709551

I *700,* Geneva, Switzerland; *55,* dewpoint is −5°F.

II *8,* 8/10 of the sky is covered by clouds; *36,* wind is from the north (360°); *04,* the wind speed is 4 knots.

III *81,* the visibility is 21⅞ statute miles (35 kilometers); *02,* present weather is "more than half the sky is covered by clouds"; *2,* past weather is the same as present weather.

IV *080,* sea level pressure is 1008.0 millibars; *01,* present temperature is 1°F.

V *1,* the amount of the lowest layer of clouds is less than 1/10, but not zero; *5,* these clouds are of the genera: stratocumulus, stratus, cumulus; *6,* these clouds are between 3,000 and 4,999 feet above the ground; *0,* there are no middle clouds; *8,* high clouds cover 10/10 of the sky.

VI *6,* group indicator; *0,* the direction from which the clouds are moving is unknown; *3,* the pressure has been falling but is now increasing; *19,* during the last 3 hours the pressure has risen 1.9 millibars.

VII 7, group indicator; *095,* 0.95 inches of rain (or snow equivalent) fell in the last 6 hours; *5,* rain (or snow) ended 5 hours ago; *1,* 1 inch of snow has accumulated on the ground at the present time.

All this information is contained in thirty-six numbers which, on a standard teletype machine, take forty-two seconds for transmission.

Many ships send similar data, except that they report their latitude and longitude position, course, and sea conditions as well. These messages are usually sent by radioteletype but may also be put on the air by ordinary hand-keyed radio transmission.

Surface data collected the world over is only a small part of the data traffic carried by telephone wires or radio. Winds-aloft information from shore and ship stations is collected and transmitted, too. In the lower layers of the atmosphere, wind speed and direction are reported for each thousand-foot layer. Higher up—to altitudes of 100,000 feet or so—winds are given for somewhat thicker layers. Then there are the pressure, temperature, and humidity data for the first 15–25 miles of atmospheric envelope resting on the surface of the earth. The messages containing these data are routine; each six or twelve hours all the meteorological stations equipped to take the measurements send their observations.

This is only the beginning. Up to this point, only transmissions of actual data have been considered. There are many, many others that carry the results of digested data as well: summaries and forecasts prepared at central weather offices with large staffs to assist the people in the field. A partial listing of some of the other coded messages may be interesting.

Area weather forecasts
Monthly climatic averages for both the surface and upper air
Ice data for northern waters
Summaries of cloud data seen by a TIROS satellite
Reports from transport aircraft and from meteorological

reconnaissance flights (of which hurricane and typhoon reports are most publicized)
Aviation route forecasts
Reports on "atmospherics"—location and intensity of lightning discharges picked up as static on specially designed direction finders
Sea-condition summaries
Seismographic earthquake reports
Radioactive-fallout forecasts (If radioactive debris were present, where would it settle)
Radarscope summaries
and many more

To assist the man in the field even more, completely analyzed maps are made available to him. In almost every weather office in this country, there is at least one facsimile machine which faithfully reproduces a tremendous number of weather maps drawn up in the weather centers. As a photoelectric eye scans the original weather map, a current is produced in high-grade telephone wires that form a spider web around the center. Whenever the eye sees a dark spot, at the receiving facsimile the current causes a slight sparking, or burning, on a moving sheet of specially prepared paper. Since the transmitting and receiving equipment are "locked" together, the burned spot appears in exactly the position where the photoelectric eye saw the original spot.

Many of the larger ships at sea have radio facsimile equipment which operate like their land counterparts. For the use of smaller ships not so equipped, a so-called "canned map" is transmitted by ordinary radio code; this permits someone aboard to draw the weather map in much the same way that children draw faces or animals by connecting dot 1 to dot 2 to dot 3 . . . .

The military services also have special weather messages

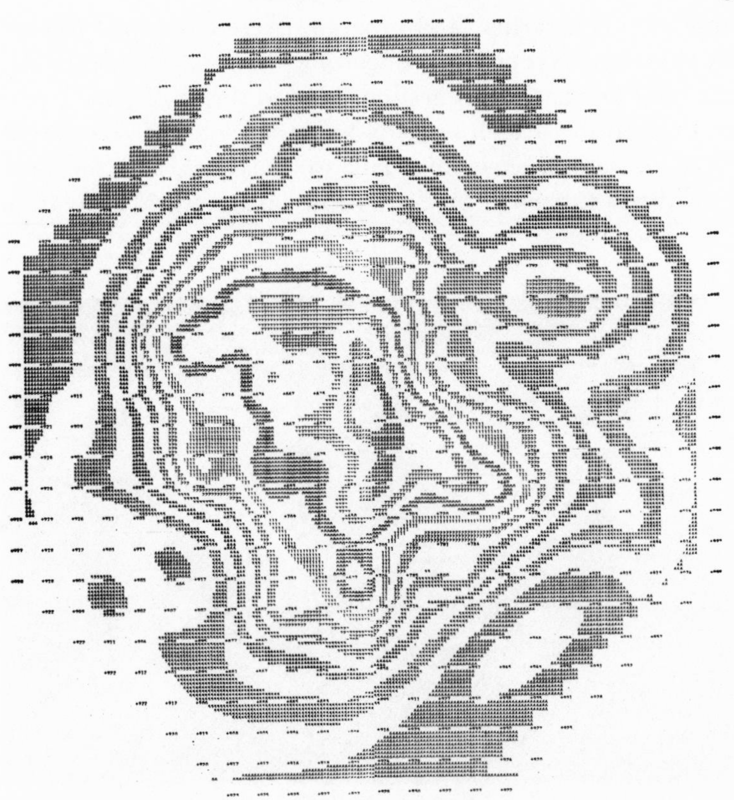

Weather Map as Produced by an Electronic Computer

applying to their military operations, such as ballistic messages that give needed wind and density corrections for bombing, gunfire, and missile trajectories, and forecasts of radar ranges.

While some of these special messages are prepared within the general area where they are to be used, the majority are made up at a central location that is quite remote. Mostly, the contents of these broadcast messages are not derived by human effort just prior to transmission. The brain power was applied much earlier, and programs were developed for use by electronic computers. Meteorological data, then, provides the food for machine digestion. Myriad sheets of paper spew forth from the machine, ready for broadcast. Between larger weather stations, machines talk to machines, and the final tally sheets extrude from equipment a half a world away from

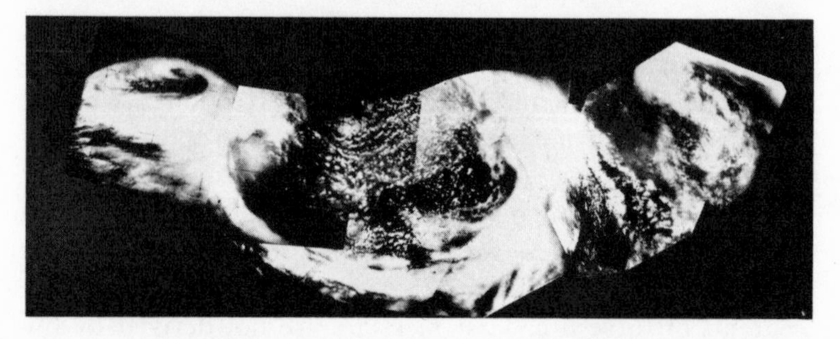

Conventional Weather Map with Satellite Input

the place where they were prepared. Were it not for the publicity given to Mariner IV and its photographs of Mars relayed to earth by numerical coding of the numbers zero and one, this daily routine used by weather offices would be more newsworthy. Essentially, the same process is involved.

These specialized forecasts may seem necessary but dull to the nonmilitary, but there is at least one type of such message that should be more interesting. The Navy routinely provides Ship-Routing Messages to ships of the Fleet and to those of the MSTS—Military Sea Transportation Service—the service which carries military personnel, their dependents, and their belongings overseas. Commercial vessels can receive the same type of data from civilian sources.

The ship-routing program is predicated on the fact that the shortest and easiest route for crossing an ocean is not necessarily the most direct one. Certainly, a great-circle course from a point on the coast of the United States to one in Europe or Asia represents the fewest number of miles, but if this course runs through a large oceanic storm, the fewest number of miles can add up to a great number of extra hours and tremendous passenger discomfort, even structural damage to the ship and its contents.

To save time, and therefore money, and to provide a happier, safer passage, the ship should be routed around the storm, but not so far around as to lengthen the distance inordinately nor so far around, or worse, on the wrong side, that advantage cannot be taken of a following sea and winds. The characteristics of each ship receiving ship-routing service have been studied so that the conditions under which it sails most easily are known. How high must waves be to produce unpleasant roll? On what quarter of the ship will a blowing wind have the most desirable effect? From knowledge of the keel length, how much pitching motion will there be if the distance between wave crests is a given amount?

Day by day, the ship captains are advised of the best route to follow. As with any innovation, there are those—independent souls, perhaps—who consider ship routing to be the invention of the devil. The percentage of garbled, and therefore, unreadable messages reported by these salty characters is phenomenal and makes one wonder whether radio is really here to stay.

There are others, however, who not only welcome these messages but rely on them heavily. An occasional truly garbled message upsets them no end. It is from these transport skippers that reports come back telling of multiple hours saved on an Atlantic crossing and multiple days saved during a Pacific voyage. And time saved means money saved.

At any rate, the air around us is almost saturated with inaudible weather messages, and that part of the radio-frequency spectrum assigned by the Federal Communications Commission for use by the weather services is packed to capacity.

11

The Weather Observer's Lot

Although some of the methods for acquiring weather data are perhaps obvious, others are more involved and not without interest. Consider the method of measuring snow or rain, for example. Neither is as easy as it would seem. The principal problem, as with any type of meteorological measurement, is one of exposure. The instruments must be so located that they can measure the unmodified atmosphere. Nearby buildings or trees can cause swirling winds that would not only affect wind speed and direction if these were being measured there, but also cause drifting of snow, trapping of too much or too little rain, and variations in temperature. The surface on which the instruments stand also influences the measurements. White sand or concrete will increase the temperature and produce eddies between it and neighboring grassy or dark areas. A black-top surface may reduce the temperature, also producing eddies. In manuals of instruction concerning the initial establishment of meteorological stations, pages and pages are devoted to the proper location of instrument shelters.

Even the construction of the shelter is narrowly defined. A louvered box is used, which is usually made of pine or a similar wood and painted white. The paint must be kept in good

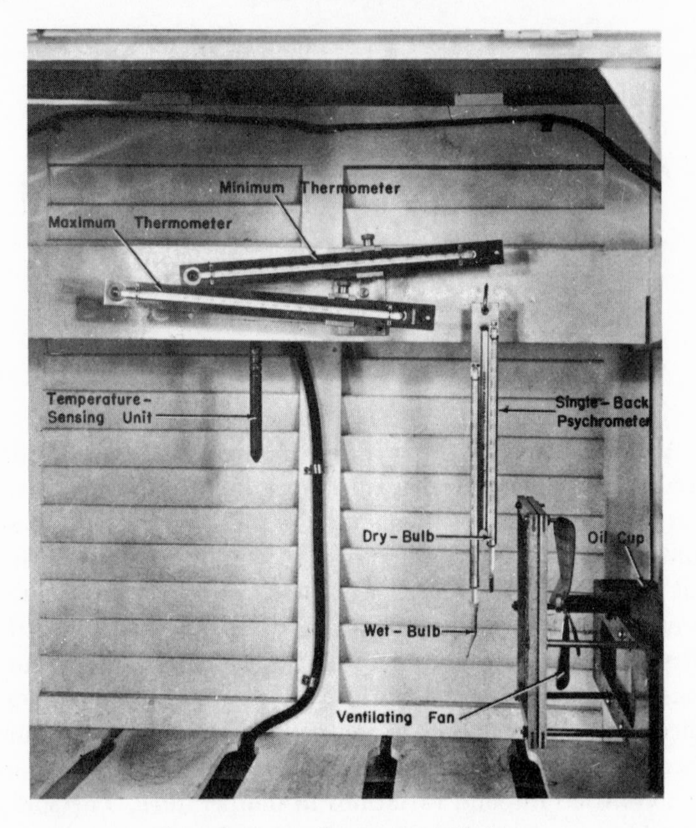

Interior of an Instrument Shelter

condition so that most of the direct solar radiation is reflected and so that the interior of the shelter does not heat unduly. The louvers are so slanted that there is no possibility of radiation proceeding in a straight line from the outside to the inside. Further, the interior ceiling is also louvered and is separated by an air space from the solid roof of the shelter.

There are more specifications. The shelter is usually supported about four feet above the ground on an open wooden framework set out in a grassy field. Even so, the air inside it is not exactly like the outside air, and measurements are a specific function of the location of the shelter. Climatologists have been made exceedingly unhappy by the increased urbanization of many of the older cities and towns. Some New England locations have had continuous records since prerevolutionary days, but the measurements, once taken in the rural fringes of the communities, became in-city measurements as the population increased. The weather station and the instrument shelter had to be moved, with a resultant loss of continuity in the records.

Currently, when a weather station is relocated, every effort is made to continue the operation of both old and new stations for a prolonged period of time. The overlapping of records helps in adjusting the earlier to the later values and provides some measure of climatological continuity.

Snowfall, however, is not measured in a shelter. It is always determined in the open, away from all obstructions that might cause drifting or sheltering. Snow depth can be determined with a ruler when snow is freshly fallen on a bare surface, but if it has fallen on snow that has been accumulating for days or weeks, the depth measurement can be in error. Snow will compact, as any child who has rolled a snowball or fashioned a snowman can testify. A sizable new snowfall can easily be heavy enough to crush the snow surface on which it falls so that the before-and-after measurements may be almost the same.

Cores of snow can be taken, using implements not unlike apple corers or bulb planters, and the measured volume of snow removed can be melted to find how much its water equivalent is. This obviates the difficulty of compacted snow. Or each new batch of snow can be caught in a gauge and melted to find how much fell in a given period of time.

With rain, the difficulty of measurement, once the exposure problem is licked, is considerably less. If the rain gauge is properly exposed and of a size and construction that is standard for all members of the World Meteorological Organization, the amount of water collected will be precise. It may not be "accurate"—that is, the actual amount of rain that fell—but it will be a value comparable to all values collected in rainfall measurements.

It will be precise, however, only if the water collected has not evaporated between the time that the precipitation stopped and the time the observer went out to inspect the rain gauge.

To preclude both the evaporation and the necessity for the observer's trip, a tipping-bucket rain gauge can be used. This ingenious device has a delicately balanced tiny bucket below

Tipping-Bucket Rain Gauge

the funnel of the rain gauge. It can support exactly 1/100 inch of water. If any more drips into the bucket, it tips, dumps out its liquid load, and rights itself again, ready to receive a new supply. Each time it tips, it makes an electric contact, which records the action in the meteorological office. To determine the amount of rain, it is necessary only to record how many times the contact was closed.

Finding a proper place for exposing wind-measuring equipment is even more tricky. At any outdoor sports arena or on any national holiday, even a casual glance at displays of flags and pennants will reveal the many apparent directions and speeds of the wind. One flag whips proudly to the east while a neighboring one drapes itself limply against its pole. A third may wave idly toward the north, or south, or any other compass point.

Even when the matter of proper exposure is overcome, there is the question of what wind speed and direction is to be recorded. The wind is never entirely constant. Even the lightest breeze is somewhat gusty, blowing slightly harder or softer in an unrhythmic pattern, coming first from one direction and then from another. The stronger the wind, the greater are the variations, both up and down. Is the correct wind velocity the one that is apparent at the instant the observer looks at the wind dials? Obviously not. Thus, the wind speed and direction must also be recorded and an average over a period of time taken. Here again, international convention dictates the time interval and method of averaging.

Temperature must be a straightforward measurement, must it not? Well, there are many different types of temperature measurements and thermometers, each serving a special purpose, but the primary problem is, again, what is the meaning of the temperature that the instrument indicates?

An interesting experiment in temperature variation was performed in Toronto, Canada. An eight-mile drive in an automobile was made as rapidly as traffic and traffic laws permitted from the lakefront northward. A sensitive thermometer was attached to the car at a height of some two feet above the street. On a clear, calm night in winter, the temperature within the eight-mile strip varied from a reading of 16° to −17°F. Within a half-mile stretch, at one point where the terrain dips sharply, there was a difference in temperature reading of about 26°F. A similar run on a cloudy summer night showed far smaller variations: only about 2°F for the same automobile trip.

What was recorded was more a variation of temperature with distance than with time. The time problem is also a real one, however. On an afternoon in late August, for example, during a period of 900 seconds (15 minutes), a thermometer hung in a properly sheltered location showed an over-all fluctuation of more than 2°F with changes of more than 1 degree occurring on the average of at least once each minute.

The current temperature is usually read just outside the in-

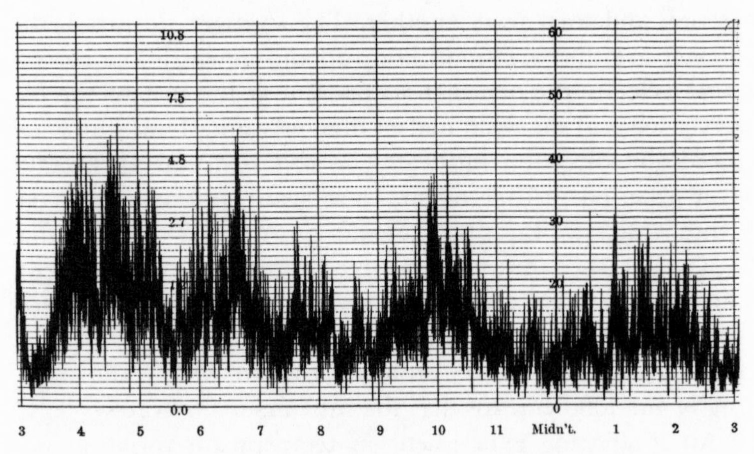

A Wind Speed Record-Speed in Miles per Hour

strument shelter. The thermometer is one of a pair supported on a metal holder complete with a short length of chain and a wooden handle. The bulb of the second thermometer is covered by a small, clean, white sock that has been dipped in water. To take the air temperature, the observer whirls this contraption at arm's length as fast as he can, stopping occasionally to read the values of both thermometers. He continues this procedure until there is no change in temperature between successive readings. The dry-bulb thermometers records the air temperature. The other thermometer, with the wet sock or wick, records the wet-bulb temperature: usually a value less than air temperature, since it is cooled by evaporation of the water into the air. From the difference between wet- and dry-bulb readings, the relative humidity can be computed. When the atmosphere is completely saturated—100 per cent relative humidity—the wet- and dry-bulb readings are the same, of course, since no evaporation takes place.

In addition to the reading of current temperature, there is considerable interest in the values of the maximum and minimum temperatures occurring during the last twenty-four hour period—the period is from 6 A.M. on one day to 6 A.M. on the next. The maximum thermometer serves the same type of function as one used to measure a patient's fever and is similarly constructed. It must hold the mercury in the tube at the highest point reached during the course of measurement regardless of subsequent temperature changes. This is accomplished by having a narrow constriction in the stem of the thermometer near the bulb. There are few forces that can withstand the pressure of an expanding liquid, so the heated mercury flows through the restriction easily enough. However, just the force of gravity is not sufficient to push the liquid back through the narrow passage, when it cools. So the mercury column stands at its highest value until it is shaken down manually.

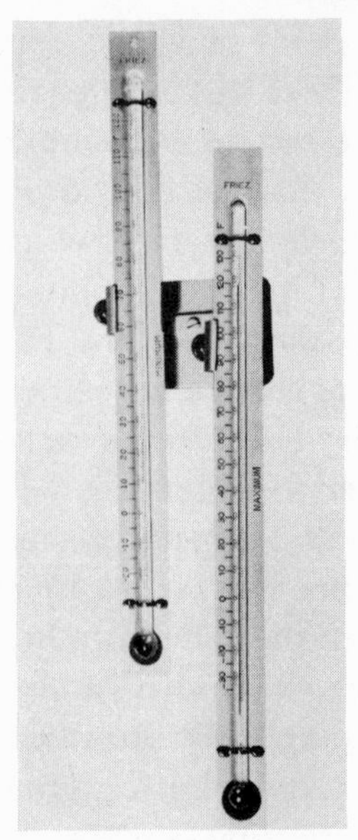

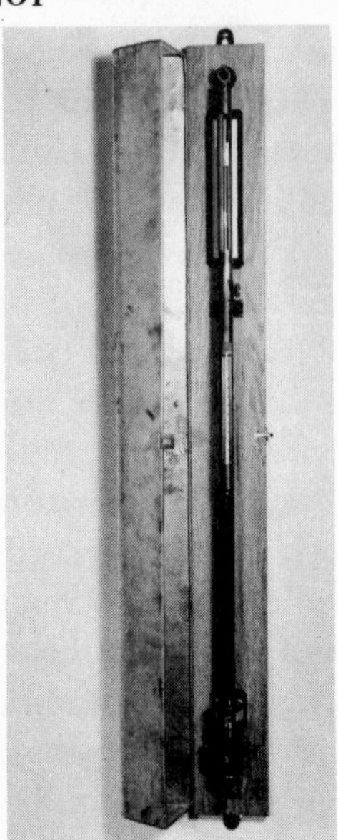

Left: *Maximum and Minimum Thermometers.* Right: *Mercury Barometer*

The minimum thermometer also works on a simple physical principle, although it functions quite differently. The topmost surface of a liquid in a tube is called the meniscus, and, depending upon whether the liquid wets the tube or not, the meniscus is curved upward or downward. (Water wets glass, and the top surface is curved downward, with the water at the edges clinging to the glass. Mercury does not wet glass, so the part touching the sides is lower than the center of the liquid.) Because of the curvature, there is an unusual play of forces on the meniscus, which in many ways acts more as though it were a membrane instead of just a part of the rest of the liquid.

To record the minimum temperature, a small bob is placed in the bore of a thermometer tube, and the thermometer is very carefully laid in a horizontal position so that gravity will neither pull the bob upward nor downward in the bore.

When the temperature falls, the thermometric liquid contracts, and the meniscus moves back toward the bulb of the thermometer. Since it acts as a membrane, it pushes the bob back ahead of it. If the temperature rises, the liquid expands and the miniscus leaves the bob in its "coldest" position. After all, the membrane pushes, it does not pull. The minimum temperature can be read, then, by noting the position of the bob. To reset the thermometer, it is only necessary to invert the tube until the bob sinks to meet the meniscus again.

Just a word of caution to the inventive. Meteorologists are well-aware of the use of thermocouples and the like for recording temperatures electrically, and they use many such devices as secondary instruments that must repeatedly be compared with primary standards calibrated by United States Bureau of Standards techniques. The difference between primary and secondary standards in measurements can, perhaps, be pointed out most conveniently by considering the measurement of atmospheric pressure. This is done most easily by the use of an aneroid barometer. The officially used aneroid is similar to the many home barometers whose glass-covered dials are rapped with a fingernail, prior to reading: Fair, or Change, or Rainy. The "innards" consist of a corrugated metal box from which most of the air has been pumped out. As the atmosphere presses more or less heavily on the broad surfaces of the box, the box collapses somewhat or expands. A pointer attached to its surface moves with the "respiration" of the aneroid cell.

However, the aneroid is not a primary instrument, and both in its construction and as a result of aging, the values read from it can be erroneous. The primary instrument is the mercury barometer. Most stations have one, and those that do not are visited at stated intervals by an inspector carrying a mercury barometer for use in checking the station equipment.

Everyone who has had a course in physics is acquainted

with the mercury barometer, but many will probably be surprised at the intricacies of its use in measuring the official atmospheric pressure. The atmosphere exerts a force, resulting from the weight of air above, which is sufficient at sea level to support approximately 33 feet of water or 30 inches of mercury. To measure this force, it is possible to fill a tube some 36 inches high with mercury and to turn this tube over in a well of mercury. The air presses down on the mercury surface in the well and this supports a column of liquid in the tube. It will not support all 36 inches, of course. Some of the mercury in the tube runs back into the well; but it will support about 30 inches, leaving a vacuum in the top part of the tube. To measure atmospheric pressure, then, it is just necessary to measure exactly the height that the mercury column extends above the liquid surface in the well. Therefore, if a good ruler is fastened next to the top of the tube, it should be possible to read the height exactly.

It sounds simple, but there are a few complications. There is free interchange between the mercury in the tube and that in the well. As the pressure increases, the surface of the latter must lower because more mercury goes into the tube, and vice versa. The height of the liquid in the well must also be known before the pressure can be measured with the ruler. The easiest way to do this, perhaps, is to suspend a small ivory pointer over this liquid and arrange the well so that it can be raised or lowered until the mercury it contains just touches the index marker. Fine! The ruler will now measure the height of the mercury column exactly.

Do we have the exact atmospheric pressure? Not quite. What is being measured really is the weight of the column of mercury, and one of the factors that makes up weight is the force of gravity. The earth is not quite a big, round ball. It is an oblate spheroid, bulging near the equator and more squat at the poles. Since gravity acts as though it were concentrated dead center in the earth, the force is less near the equator, where the center is farther away, and greater at the poles, where it is nearer. For places in between, the value of gravity lies between the extreme values. In order to get the exact atmospheric pressure reading, we will have to look up the latitude of the place where the measurement is being made and correct the height of the column accordingly.

While we are about it, a thought had better be given to altitude as well. What is the elevation of the station and where are we with respect to this station elevation? The barometer may be hung, for example, one-third of the way up the wall of a room on the second floor of a building standing on a small knoll. Station elevation, incidentally, is the height ten feet above the runway if this is an airport weather office. The idea is that when a plane is standing on the runway, its altimeter, which is presumed to be ten feet above the runway, will show the exact and proper reading for the elevation above sea level. So corrections for station elevation are made.

Still we are not finished. Mercury, the liquid used in many thermometers, expands and contracts with changes in temperature. Certainly, the height of the column being measured depends upon the temperature. A small thermometer had better be tacked next to the ruler on the wall so that the proper adjustments for the temperature of the mercury—and for the temperature of the ruler, as well—can be made. The ruler, too, will contract and expand.

After making all these corrections, we are getting close to the exact measurement of atmospheric pressure. There are still a few other corrections that could be incorporated, but for normal use in distributing pressure data, the job is finished. Needless to say, there are tables, scales, and a variety of computational aids to help the observer in reporting atmospheric pressure so that he need not be a surveyor or an arithmetic genius to obtain the necessary data.

There is one observational area, however, where he gets very little assistance and where skill is acquired only after years of experience and much study. This involves reporting cloud formations. The observer must describe the appearance of the sky in terms of lower, middle, and upper clouds. He has thirty code numbers that he can use, ten for each level, and he must make the selections correctly. To learn his business, he has to spend hours studying cloud atlases and definitions as well as many additional hours in discussion with other, more experienced observers.

There are many definitions prepared for his use, both in scientific jargon and in nontechnical language. The type of high cloud coded with the number "1," for example, is defined officially as "Cirrus fibratus, sometimes uncinus, not progressively invading the sky." The words are musical and

Stormy Sky

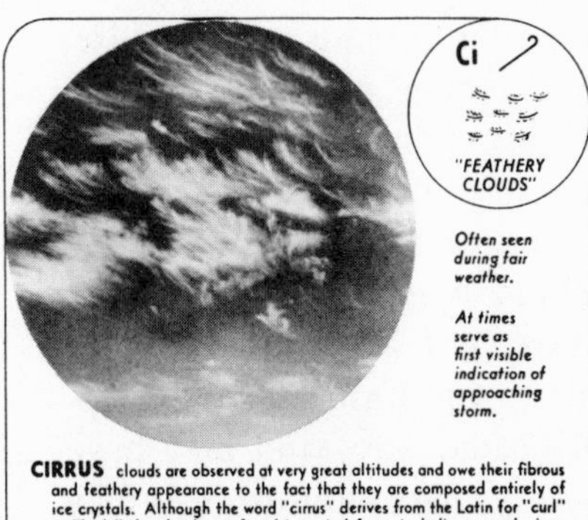

CIRRUS clouds are observed at very great altitudes and owe their fibrous and feathery appearance to the fact that they are composed entirely of ice crystals. Although the word "cirrus" derives from the Latin for "curl" or "lock," the clouds are found in varied forms including curved wisps, featherlike plumes, isolated tufts, and thin lines. Because of their height, they color before other clouds at sunrise and remain lighted after sunset.

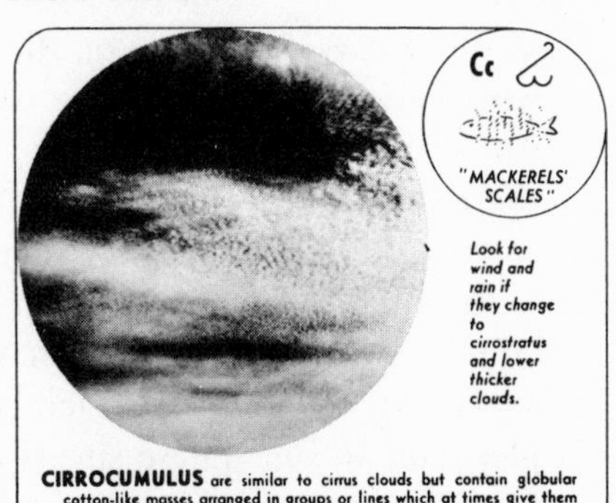

CIRROCUMULUS are similar to cirrus clouds but contain globular cotton-like masses arranged in groups or lines which at times give them the appearance of rippled sand on the seashore. One form of cirrocumulus is commonly known as the "mackerel sky" because of the way in which the pattern resembles the scales on the back of a mackerel. The harder and grayer variety, often indicate foul weather may follow.

have an obscure poetic quality but, except for the cloud expert, do not convey much meaning. The parallel nontechnical definition is rather more meaningful. "Cirrus in the form of filaments, strands, or hooks, not progressively invading the sky." Because so many of us like to watch the sky and the everchanging appearance of clouds that parade across that blue backdrop, let us describe, in nontechnical terms, some of the more general types.

First, there are the *cirrus* clouds. They are composed of ice crystals and may occur in the form of thin fibers or filaments. These may be nearly straight, irregularly curved, or seemingly entangled in a capricious manner. The fibers are sometimes shaped like a comma, terminating at the top in a hook, or in a tuft that is not rounded. Cirrus clouds also occur in patches sufficiently dense to appear greyish, when viewed toward the sun; this type of cirrus may also veil the sun, obscure its outline, or even hide it. Often the elements of cirrus arrange themselves in broad, parallel bands, converging toward the horizon.

At all times of day, cirrus not too close to the horizon is white, in fact whiter than any other cloud in the same part of the sky. With the sun on the horizon, it tends to stay white, while lower clouds may be tinted orange or yellow. As the sun drops below the horizon, cirrus clouds will go through their color transformation: yellow to pink to red and, finally, to grey. At dawn, the color sequence is reversed.

Another form of ice-crystal cloud is *cirrocumulus.* Cirrocumulus generally occurs in more or less extensive sheets, consisting of very small elements in the form of grains, ripples, and so on. These sheets are often wavy and may have fibrous margins. On rare occasions, a cirrocumulus sheet may show small, more or less regularly distributed, round holes that often give the cloud the appearance of a net or a honeycomb. Often, cirrocumulus occurs in lens- or almond-shaped patches that are very elongated and have well-defined outlines. The clouds are always transparent enough to reveal the position of the sun or the moon.

When a transparent, whitish cloud veil of fibrous or hairlike appearance totally or partly covers the sky, usually producing a halo, *cirrostratus* is present. Cirrostratus is never thick enough to prevent objects on the ground from casting shadows except when the sun is low.

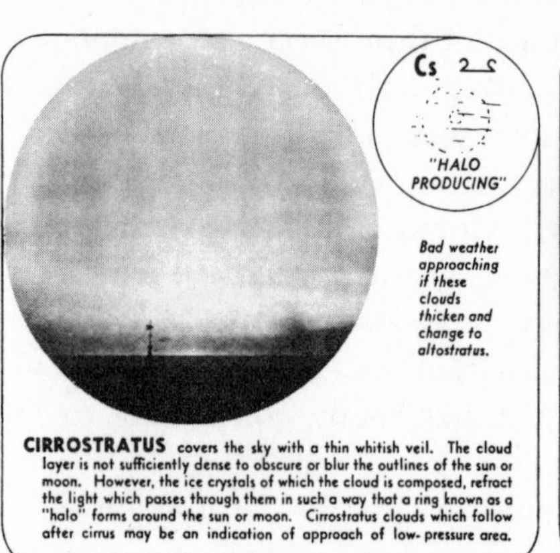

CIRROSTRATUS covers the sky with a thin whitish veil. The cloud layer is not sufficiently dense to obscure or blur the outlines of the sun or moon. However, the ice crystals of which the cloud is composed, refract the light which passes through them in such a way that a ring known as a "halo" forms around the sun or moon. Cirrostratus clouds which follow after cirrus may be an indication of approach of low-pressure area.

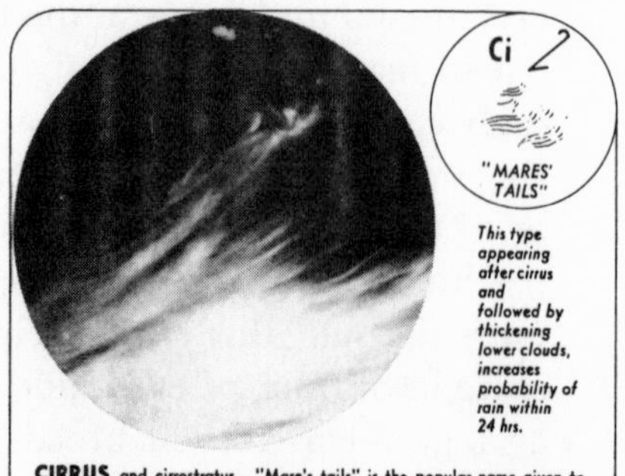

CIRRUS and cirrostratus. "Mare's tails" is the popular name given to well-defined cirrus clouds that thicken into cirrostratus, and then gradually lowering into water droplet altostratus. The clouds may resemble a mare's tail and may often be the forerunner of a storm as indicated in the old rhyme: "Mackerel sky and *mare's tails*, make tall ships carry low sails." The more brush-like the cirrus, the stronger the wind at that level.

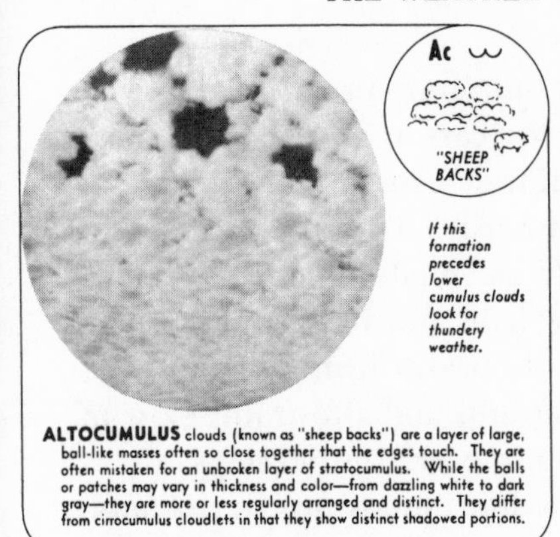

ALTOCUMULUS clouds (known as "sheep backs") are a layer of large, ball-like masses often so close together that the edges touch. They are often mistaken for an unbroken layer of stratocumulus. While the balls or patches may vary in thickness and color—from dazzling white to dark gray—they are more or less regularly arranged and distinct. They differ from cirrocumulus cloudlets in that they show distinct shadowed portions.

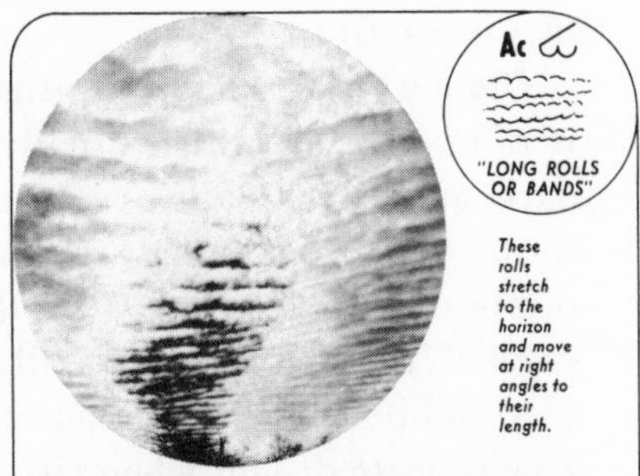

ALTOCUMULUS—in "bands" or "long rolls"—are shown above. This is a form of this cloud type having big roll clouds separated by streaks of blue sky. The rolls appear to be joined together near the horizon because of the effect of perspective. These regular parallel bands of altocumulus differ from the "mackerel sky" in that it is found in larger masses with shadows and is not composed of ice crystals like the higher cirrus forms.

While cirrus clouds may often form by the blowing off of the tops of thunderstorm clouds (*cumulonimbus*), cirrocumulus clouds, especially those in the shape of lenses or almonds, are often the result of local orographic lifting of a layer of moist air. Cirrostratus, on the other hand, is formed as a result of the slow ascent of extensive layers of air to sufficiently high levels, as in advance of a warm frontal passage.

While the three types of cirrus clouds are so-called high clouds and composed of ice crystals, altocumulus, altostratus, and nimbostratus are considered middle clouds and are composed mainly of liquid water. *Altostratus* is nearly always of great horizontal extent, covering hundreds of miles, and of fairly considerable vertical thickness. Usually, it is so dense that even through its thinner parts the sun can only be seen vaguely, although the thicker parts always mask the sun entirely. It is a precipitating cloud and trails of wisps, called virga, can be seen streaming below it. Often, the precipitation reaches to the ground and continuous rain, distinct from a shower, results. Ragged shreds of clouds can often be seen below a layer of altostratus. Like its more lofty relative, cirrostratus, it usually results from the lifting of moist air ahead of a warm front.

Closely related to altostratus but more dismal weatherwise is *nimbostratus*, which usually appears as an extensive, low, dark grey layer with a very diffuse base from which rain, snow, or ice pellets fall continuously. The undersurface of nimbostratus is often partially or totally hidden by low, ragged clouds that form at the base and change shape rapidly. While the intersection of the warm front with the surface is quite distant when cirrostratus and altostratus exist in the sky, it is close at hand when nimbostratus develops.

The cloud forms classified as low clouds are stratocumulus, stratus, cumulus, and cumulonimbus, although the last runs the gamut from lowest to highest, often having a base at a few thousand feet and a top at forty thousand or more feet. Still, because of its base, it is classed as a low cloud. *Stratocumulus* has few characteristics that make it noteworthy. It most often appears as a sheet, or layer, composed of cloudlets similar to those of altocumulus but at a lower level and, therefore, apparently larger. It is sometimes accompanied by precipitation, but more often it is just an ugly grey sky composed of tessellations, rounded masses, and rolls

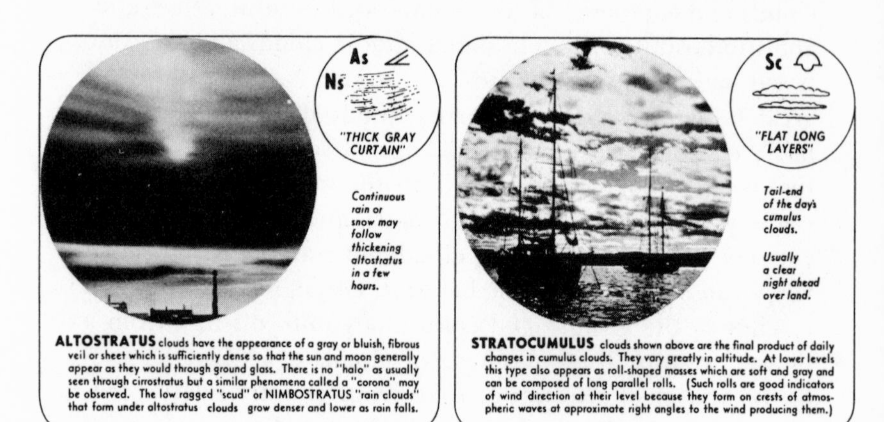

ALTOSTRATUS clouds have the appearance of a gray or bluish, fibrous veil or sheet which is sufficiently dense so that the sun and moon generally appear as they would through ground glass. There is no "halo" as usually seen through cirrostratus but a similar phenomena called a "corona" may be observed. The low ragged "scud" or NIMBOSTRATUS "rain clouds" that form under altostratus clouds grow denser and lower as rain falls.

STRATOCUMULUS clouds shown above are the final product of daily changes in cumulus clouds. They vary greatly in altitude. At lower levels this type also appears as roll-shaped masses which are soft and gray and can be composed of long parallel rolls. (Such rolls are good indicators of wind direction at their level because they form on crests of atmospheric waves at approximate right angles to the wind producing them.)

that may or may not be merged.

Stratus also gives a grey sky, but it is much more uniformly grey, and although the technical descriptions are fairly verbose, nothing seems to describe it more accurately than the words "a fog bank that has not extended to the ground."

Of all the clouds, the ones that are probably best known to the nonmeteorologist are the ones which belong to the *cumulus* family. These may be the small, innocuous fair-weather clouds of small vertical extent and bizarre shapes, or they may grow through a series of small protuberances and sproutings to become quite large clouds with bulging upper parts frequently resembling a cauliflower. Delightfully, the smallest variety are called *cumulus humilis* while, more prosaically, the larger are known as *cumulus mediocris* and *cumulus congestus.*

When the larger type grows into heavy and dense clouds in the form of a mountain with huge towers, it becomes a *cumulonimbus,* or thunderstorm. The top part of the cloud suddenly becomes quite smooth and fibrous or striated, spreading out in the shape of an anvil or vast plume. The cumulonimbus has everything in it: rain, hail, lightning, snow, and high winds.

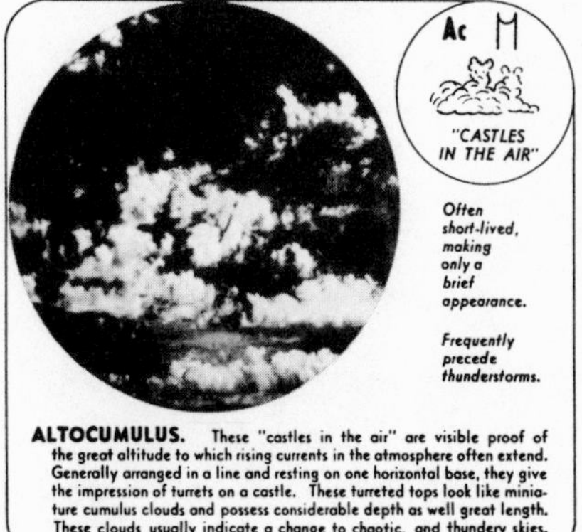

ALTOCUMULUS. These "castles in the air" are visible proof of the great altitude to which rising currents in the atmosphere often extend. Generally arranged in a line and resting on one horizontal base, they give the impression of turrets on a castle. These turreted tops look like miniature cumulus clouds and possess considerable depth as well great length. These clouds usually indicate a change to chaotic, and thundery skies.

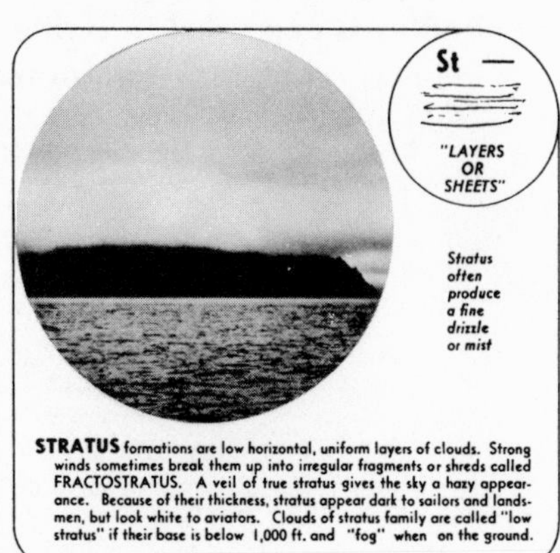

STRATUS formations are low horizontal, uniform layers of clouds. Strong winds sometimes break them up into irregular fragments or shreds called FRACTOSTRATUS. A veil of true stratus gives the sky a hazy appearance. Because of their thickness, stratus appear dark to sailors and landsmen, but look white to aviators. Clouds of stratus family are called "low stratus" if their base is below 1,000 ft. and "fog" when on the ground.

CUMULUS clouds pictured above are the small, fluffy, "fair weather type." *The various types of clouds in the cumulus family are defined according to the extent of their vertical development—the height to which warm moist air is being raised by updrafts within them.* It is the presence of these updrafts which makes flying near or in cumulus clouds "bumpy" and sometimes dangerous. Note little vertical development.

CUMULONIMBUS "thunderheads" or "showerclouds" are heavy masses of clouds rising in mountainous towers to great heights. The upper parts consist of ice crystals and often spread out in the shape of an anvil. The base is horizontal, but as showers occur it lowers and becomes ragged. The anvil of this giant cloud is so high that it can be seen many miles away long before the base becomes visible. A regular "cloud factory."

Needless to say, we have just begun to touch on some of the duties and skills required of the weather observer, who is really in the lowest echelon of the meteorological profession. It would be pointless to continue following the various procedures by which he gets the data required by the more senior members of his profession and by the insatiable electronic computers. What has been said should be sufficient to show that even at the observer's level, the work requires considerable skill and ingenuity and that a tremendous amount of effort is expended in trying to get the wherewithal to provide accurate weather information.

12

Making and Breaking Clouds

Now to talk about the atmospheric subject that interests me most. Anyone with whom I discourse on this subject should, as a matter of self-protection, be aware not only that I have worked hard and earnestly in this field but also that I tend to ride a hobby horse. One result of my labors and dedication is that in addition to acquiring a considerable fund of knowledge and experience, I have also had the opportunity to develop a substantial number of opinions—some of which are not generally accepted. I also try hard to play fair and not ride that hobby horse surreptitiously. As I talk, I sincerely endeavor to separate fact from fiction and knowledge from opinion by the judicious use of "I think" and "it seems to me."

Planned, contrived weather—call it weather modification, weather control, or climate control—is my subject. My interest puts me into a well-populated category of human beings clearly and properly labeled as quacks and charlatans as well as in a very sparse congregation of reputable scientists working on this exciting aspect of weather science. Sometimes, it is very difficult to decide easily which are which, and I, for one, would hesitate to pin a label on some of those who work in weather control. Perhaps the best criterion might be that those who claim that they can achieve or have achieved significant results are questionable. To my knowledge, no important degree of weather modification has yet been demonstrated.

There are many, however, who occupy a limbo where, while they make no extravagant claims, imply sufficient success to induce farmers, ranchers, and even cities to pay them large sums of money in the effort to order the kind of weather—usually wet—that is desired. This ambivalent behavior makes for marvelously complicated law suits in New York, Texas, and elsewhere when one group of the citizenry sues the "rainmaker" and his customers for damages resulting from some ruinous storm. The rainmaker must disclaim responsibility for the destructive weather in such a way as to convince a jury of his professional ineffectiveness without simultaneously convincing those who pay for his services of the same point.

However, no discussion of the ethics and scientific integrity of rainmakers of any persuasion can be considered finished until the revered name of Irving Langmuir, an eminent scientist and Nobel Prize winner, is brought into prominence. He pioneered the field of weather modification. Without the luster of his sterling international reputation to reflect respectability, the number of serious scientists working in direct atmospheric experimentation would be seriously reduced.

Drawing the mantle of the late Irving Langmuir tightly about me, let me make a few remarks about terminology. Weather control and weather modification are terms that frequently are used interchangeably but which, although they overlap considerably, should be kept separate. In essence, weather modification is a one-shot deal. Nature provides a certain weather situation. The scientist modifies it and then, presumably, goes away, leaving the atmosphere to nature again. Weather control is a protracted business in which, day after day, perhaps year after year, the atmosphere is repeatedly modified in order to control one or more aspects of its behavior. If fog appears over an airport and it is dispersed sufficiently to permit aircraft landings, this is weather modification. If an attempt is made to prevent fog from ever appearing at that airport, it is an effort at weather control.

Another distinction that can be made with propriety involves scale. Working with one or a few scattered clouds should be categorized as weather modification. On the other hand, the steering or the destruction of a large cyclonic storm, such as a hurricane or a northeaster, would probably qualify as weather control.

Although climate control is frequently used as a third kind of goal for atmospheric experimentation, I can see no great difference between weather control and climate control. If someone can keep fog from occurring at a given place for a significant period of time, he has altered, and therefore controlled, the climate of that locale. Climatological statistics would reflect: occurrence of fog—0 per cent, whereas earlier the number would have been larger. Similarly, if the weather over the Sahara could be controlled sufficiently to produce regular rainfall, the desert climate that now prevails would certainly be altered.

One last point must be made by way of introduction. Depending upon the degree of purism in which one may be inclined to indulge, weather modification is not very new nor always very dramatic. Even the most puristic would probably not consider electric or gas air-conditioning systems as weather control, but they may hesitate in assessing the activities of citrus growers in Florida or California who light smudge pots on a frosty night. The black, smoky pall reduces radiation from the ground and keeps the surface temperature somewhat higher—hopefully above freezing—than it would otherwise be. Is that weather modification? How does one assess the planting of a row of trees to serve as a windbreak?

Should the intricate network of irrigation ditches in the southwest be called weather modification or control? Probably not. The Department of the Interior and most atmospheric scientists call the reverse situation by one of those titles, however. The loss of water by evaporation from ponds and lakes during a hot, dry summer is horrendous in parts of the country where water is often at a premium. To cut down on the evaporation, it is not unusual for small ponds to be run together to form a lake. This has the effect of presenting a much smaller total surface area from which water evaporates, even though substantially the same volume of water is involved. This. of course, no one calls weather modification, but for several years, experimenters have tried to reduce the exposed water surface area by putting a film of non-evaporative material on the pond or lake. One such attempt, at least, did not work out. The additive provided a delectable treat to the resident fish. It was perhaps the most expensive fish-feeding enterprise in history, but it was supported by weather-modification funds and coordinated by weather-modification committees.

Facetiously, I suggested that the planting of trees as a windbreak might be called weather control. Again, using the money budgeted for research in this aspect of atmospheric science, the naked borders of some of these lakes were planted with special vegetation that would, presumably, reduce the air flow over the water surface and, because of the more static condition, cut down on evaporation. It worked, too. Unfortunately, as the vegetation developed, its demand for water grew as well. The experimenters were not certain at the end whether the new growth used up more water than was saved by the reduction of the wind flow.

Enough of that. You and I know what we mean when we talk of weather modification. We mean rainmaking, primarily. We mean attacking a cloud and making it let loose its cargo of water to the earth below. Or we mean preventing rain on the opening day of the World Series. We mean cutting down a thunderstorm before it reaches its prime in order to reduce its potentiality for generating hail, lightning, and tornadoes. We also mean the infanticide of hurricanes.

Let us talk about these, considering the attacks on clouds first. As a start, some knowledge of cloud development is necessary. Earlier, I emphasized that clouds form when air is lifted—by the passage of a front, by being forced over a mountain range, or by heating from below. But what really happens?

When moist air is forced upward by any mechanism, it cools. As the temperature drops, the air can hold less and less water in the vapor, or gaseous, form, so that air which started as unsaturated comes closer to saturation as it moves upward. Eventually, a temperature is reached at which the mass of air holds all the water vapor it possibly can and any further cooling should produce condensation. Should? Water droplets cannot be formed simply by adding one water molecule onto another and another until a macroscopic globule is formed. Droplets require a nucleus for formation, a particle of some foreign substance onto which the first few water molecules can adhere and on which the droplet can grow.

In carefully cleaned air, under laboratory conditions, such nuclei are absent, and air can be significantly supersaturated. Indeed, one of the ways of determining the presence of radioactivity, for example, is to have a chamber of such supersaturated air and watch the tiny cloud streaks develop as the passage of a radioactive particle provides the nuclei for condensation. In the atmosphere, however, there is no dearth of condensation nuclei anywhere. Salt particles resulting from the evaporation of sea spray, dust particles, radioactive materials (from natural sources for eons prior to the first atomic explosion), and volcanic ash abound in the atmosphere.

There are always more than enough nuclei to permit the condensation of water in saturated air. Thus, when air rises beyond the point of saturation, water droplets always form. Indeed, there is such a superabundance of nuclei that limitless numbers of small droplets form rather than a relatively few large drops.

Any ordinary nonprecipitating cloud may have as many as 30 to 90 million such droplets in every cubic foot, and each droplet has a diameter of no more than 8/10,000 of an inch. If more water condenses, more droplets form, making the cloud bigger, without significantly changing either the size of the drops or their concentration.

The droplets are so tiny that they show no tendency to settle under the influence of gravity. The tiniest air movements are sufficient to offset any settling on their part. Their small size enables them to move in a smooth, streamlined fashion. When random motion seems to set two on a collision course, they do not collide but slip smoothly past each other without any apparent interaction. So there they are: not falling, not growing—for all their motion, essentially static.

The cloud grows or it does not. The usual summer routine begins with the formation of small, puffy clouds in the morning. These reach up into the relatively dry air above the surface and eventually evaporate. But heating of the ground continues, forcing the development of another cloud that also reaches up, higher this time, not only because the rising air is slightly less dry, but also because the air it encounters benefited from the moisture donated by the initial cloud. This cloud, too, will evaporate. The process of developing and dissipating clouds continues as long as the ground is baked by the sun and moisture is available. Eventually—usually by midafternoon—a cloud may grow tall enough to reach a critical level in the atmosphere: the level at which water freezes or ice melts: 0°C or 32°F.

What happens when the cloud bursts through this critical temperature level? Nothing. The cloud droplets ignore their obligation to turn to ice. If heat and moisture are still abundantly available, they go on their merry way, reaching higher in the atmosphere, still tiny, still non-colliding, still liquid water. But they are now vulnerable; their existence is threatened. They are now in a temperature zone where they do not belong in the form in which they exist. We may anticipate action.

Two factors may cause these water droplets to change. First, the colder they become, the more difficult it is for them to remain liquid. Almost any perturbation, if the temperature is sufficiently below freezing, many jar them into ice. Indeed, it is just about impossible to cool liquid water droplets, even under laboratory conditions, below −40° (Fahrenheit or Centigrade—the two temperature scales are identical at this value). In the atmosphere, of course, the droplets do not have a chance to get this cold without solidifying. Some accident happens to them much earlier.

The accident may be a jarring motion of some kind. An aircraft passing, for example, could do it, in which case the wings of the plane would receive a coating of ice. But the more likely accident is a collision with a particle of some foreign substance floating in the air. Nuclei are necessary for the condensation of liquid water from water vapor; those which accomplish this transformation are called condensation nuclei, and they are plentiful. In general, however, they are completely ineffective in transforming liquid to solid water. Other kinds of nuclei are required for this, called freezing nuclei or sublimation nuclei, and these are far more sparsely represented in the atmosphere. The collision that takes place, then, is with a freezing nucleus.

A variety of atmospheric contaminants can convert liquid to ice, and some of the following substances have been identified at the center of an atmospheric ice crystal: loam, clay, loess, sand, agate, and ash. Silicates are thought to be particularly effective since they share a hexagonal crystal structure with ice. The degree of effectiveness of any given material can be measured by determining the temperature at which glaciation, or ice formation, takes place. The closer this is to the freezing temperature of water, the more effective is the nucleus. The experimental setup required is quite simple. A deep-freeze box is lined with black material and the air within allowed to reach a predetermined low temperature. While a flashlight is held for illumination, you exhale into the cooled volume of air, injecting water vapor. The "steam" shows up as clearly as one's breath on a cold morning. Now, you introduce a small amount of nuclei test material. If it serves its purpose, the dull-appearing "steam" changes instantly to sparkling diamonds in the flashlight beam.

Well, the atmosphere contains variable quantities of different freezing nuclei. When the cloud reaches levels cold enough to make them effective, a few of the water droplets change to ice. Momentarily, the cloud contains many tiny liquid water drops and a few tiny ice crystals. But not for long! This mixture is most unstable.

The instability results from the differing rates of evaporation and condensation (or sublimation) between liquid water and ice. Always, throughout their lives, the liquid droplets have been exchanging water with the surrounding atmosphere. A few molecules of water would evaporate from the droplet's surface and be replaced by condensation of an equal number from the saturated air in which the droplet floated. The balance of molecules evaporating and condensing remained intact so that the droplet neither grew nor diminished. Water vapor also evaporates from an ice surface and is replated on the surface by the surrounding atmosphere. This is called sublimation, since the change is directly from gas to solid or reverse. At temperatures below freezing, however, the rate at which water molecules leave an ice surface is much slower than that at which they leave a liquid surface. By the same token, the rate at which they plate out on ice is much greater than that at which they return to a liquid surface at the same below-freezing temperature.

What happens then in our cloud which has both liquid and solid water in its upper reaches? The ice crystals grow at the expense of the liquid droplets. Water molecules leaving the droplet will tend to settle on the ice crystals. With amazing rapidity, the entire top of the cloud turns to ice. The transformation can be observed easily on an afternoon when large clouds grow in the sky. The hard, sharp appearance of a growing cloud turret composed of liquid water drops suddenly turns silky, diffuse, and fuzzy. Water has turned to ice.

But there are relatively few sublimation nuclei. This means there is by no means a one to one relationship between ice crystals and water droplets. Each ice crystal serves many droplets, picking up water from them all, growing large, and growing heavy: too heavy to float serenely as did the droplets. Under the influence of gravity, they begin to fall. Down they go, settling finally to layers in the atmosphere where temperatures are above freezing. Slow as the inception of ice formation may have been, there is no corresponding reluctance of the ice particles to melt. As they fall, they return to a liquid state, but now they are no longer only 8/10,000 inch in diameter. They are quite sizable. They no longer slip about in ballet-like streamlined flow, but crash about like a bull in a china shop. Tiny liquid droplets in the lower part of the cloud cannot dodge them as they fall but are gathered up to make the erstwhile ice mass—now liquid—even larger. They become too large to remain as single drops. The giant globules shatter and form several smaller drops, each still huge compared to normal cloud droplets. They continue on their crashing, downward courses and in turn break up when they, too, grow large enough. A chain reaction has been initiated so that more and more sizable drops form. It is raining. Below, people will rush for shelter or put up their umbrellas.

In middle latitudes, this is always the way in which rain develops. Always, at some point in the process, ice was involved. Need it be said that a snow storm develops in the same manner? The difference is only that when the pellets fall, they never encounter temperatures above freezing so that they, now grown lacy and fragile by the accretion of water vapor, do not melt before reaching the ground.

Almost all the cloud-seeding experiments make use of this natural mechanism, helping nature with her work. Most of the attempts to modify weather attack the top part of a cloud which, while it is below freezing, has not yet changed to ice. The effort is to bring about that change artificially.

Dry ice was the first seeding material. It is effective because of its low temperature. Solid carbon dioxide maintains a temperature of −78°C. When it has been crushed and ejected into the air from an airplane, the dry ice particles fall, each one cooling a tiny column of air in its passage. Since liquid-water droplets tend to change to ice spontaneously when temperatures drop far enough below freezing, the passage of a dry-ice pellet leaves a column of water-ice crystals in its wake. The cloud now has the requisite "explosive" mixture of ice and water at below freezing temperatures, and nature takes its course.

A few moments of consideration of the mechanism will produce a precaution that must be observed when dry ice or any other seeding agent is used. Too many nuclei must not be released. If a cloud is overseeded, no single crystal will grow sufficiently to fall. An ice-crystal cloud in lieu of a water-droplet cloud would be produced. This precaution holds not only in rainmaking but also in the clearance of supercooled fog. While almost all fog encountered in midlatitudes occurs at temperatures above freezing, Arctic regions do occasionally have liquid-water fog at below-freezing temperatures. These fogs can be seeded and cleared up, but woe unto the person doing the seeding if he simply changes each liquid-water droplet into a corresponding ice crystal. Fog may be a severe obstruction to visibility, but shimmering, light-scattering ice crystals are infinitely worse.

Because of the short life span of solid carbon dioxide, the only practical way of dispersing it into the upper part of clouds is from an airplane. Needless to say, this is the difficult and expensive way to seed clouds. Weather modifiers sought another seeding material: one that they might be able to dispense at ground level and which could persist so that natural air movements would carry it upward.

Silver iodide was the answer. Its principal virtues are the ease with which volumes of it can be produced and its effectiveness in nucleating ice crystals. Silver iodide seems to do the latter by deception. In certain aspects, a silver iodide crystal is almost identical to an ice crystal, having the same hexagonal arrangement and essentially the same interatomic distances. The poor gullible water molecules are unable to tell the difference between silver iodide and solid water and will crystallize as readily on the one as on the other. Again, once a few ice crystals are present in the liquid-water cloud, regardless of whether water or silver iodide is at their core, the necessary conditions for cloud dissipation (and rain) are met.

Let us pause for a moment and think about the words "cloud dissipation and rain." At various times, I, too, have knocked a cloud out of the sky. Always, in reporting my feat, I was careful to say "I dissipated a cloud." Always, a non-meteorologist would immediately ask "Did you make it rain?" My answer just as inevitably provoked the kind of shrug of the shoulder that said, "What can you expect of a scientific character? They can no more give a straight answer than a politician can." This response was invoked by my saying that I did not know or by my countering with "What is rain?"

A scientist can, on occasion, be convinced that he has produced large water drops in a cloud and that this process destroyed the cloud. Without observers below on the ground, he cannot be certain that the falling water actually reached the ground. Frequently, it rains out of a cloud base, but the water evaporates between the cloud and the earth's surface so that only the lightest sprinkle, if any, is noted by those below. Also, how much water must fall before it is called rain? For the most part, the types of clouds experimenters fly into or over for seeding experiments are relatively small; large clouds are too hazardous. A cloud approximately a mile or two wide, deep, and tall does not rate as very much on nature's scale of cloud sizes. If all the water were squeezed out of such a cloud, the amount of rainfall would still be quite limited. The rain would be over almost as fast as you could react by opening your umbrella.

Experimentally, nothing so subjective is used as a criterion of effectiveness. The rainmaking question is answered in another way. A region is selected for experimentation where the prevalence of appropriate clouds is quite high. At the surface, an extensive network of rain gauges is set up so that there is a great probability of catching a sample of all precipitation in the area. A flight procedure is developed specifying exactly the patterns the seeding aircraft will fly and those that will be flown by observer aircraft. Thus, everything is set up for the rainmaking experiment.

Each day the meteorologist with the program makes his forecast as to whether the next day will be a good one for seeding or not. If his forecast calls for suitable weather, on the next day the aircraft take off on their assigned missions.

Just before take-off, however, someone opens a safe in which are a number of sealed envelopes. He selects one at random and hands it to the "seeding" officer on the seeding plane. When the plane is airborne, this individual opens the envelope and reads one of two possible messages. The envelope contains a card saying either "Seed" or "Don't seed."

No one else associated with the program knows what the instructions are. The routine followed by planes and men is identical except that if the card said "Don't seed" nothing is ejected from the seeding plane. Observers observe; rain gauges measure.

The next day that is propitious for seeding, the same flights and observations are made, but this time, no envelope is chosen. If on the earlier flight seeding took place, none will take place on the second flight. If the first of the pair of flights has been a dry run, the second will be a seeding flight. Thus, through an entire season, flights in pairs are conducted with all personnel save one ignorant of which were the seeding days.

At the end of the season, the scores are tallied. What the observers saw on seeded days is compared with what they saw on unseeded ones. More significantly, the rain-gauge measurements for each kind of day are compared. The results are fascinating. One year, the rain gauges will show perhaps 50 per cent more rain falling on seeded days. The next year, to everyone's dismay, the amount of precipitation on the seeded days may be significantly less than on the unseeded ones. During a third year, there may be no meaningful difference.

All manner of hypotheses are offered to explain these haphazard results. Perhaps the rain-gauge network was not extensive or dense enough to catch all the rain. After all, the seeding has to take place upwind of the network so that the cloud will have blown over the gauges when the rain begins to fall. Perhaps the scientists and pilots misjudged either the speed of the wind or the rate of rainfall development. Perhaps the seeding agent had deteriorated. And so it goes on without anyone reaching a conclusion. Most of the more reputable scientists have withdrawn from this fray, announcing that not enough is known about atmospheric processes to justify experimentation in the atmosphere. They have taken themselves back into their laboratories to learn more about the fundamentals of cloud physics.

I have my own explanation, which not only accounts for the facts but also points the way to a future for weather modification. It seems to me that any one who has spent a long, lazy day at the beach watching the sky should understand what is happening. The natural course of cloud development is the alternate building and evaporation of the clouds, starting with small and insignificant ones early in the day and larger and larger ones following as the day wears on. Eventually, one cloud grows big enough to produce a shower. Generally, this completes the cloud cycle for the day, since by then the sun is sufficiently low in the sky that it no longer is able to supply the energy for more cloud build-ups.

If we think of this as a cyclic process, labels could be attached to each stage. Thus the small, puffy clouds of the early morning could be labeled *A*, while the larger clouds could be given the letters *B, C, D,* and so on, according to size. Let us suppose that it is cloud size *G* that extends high enough into the colder reaches of the atmosphere to achieve the ice stage and produce precipitation. In his efforts to modify a cloud, the experimenter attacks not cloud *G* but an earlier one in the series: *E* or *F*. Even if he is successful in producing rain, he can still only produce less from his smaller cloud than nature can from a larger one.

In effect, if every summer day of that type ended with a rain shower, the rain gauges would always collect less precipitation on the days when man seeded the clouds than when the clouds were permitted to continue their development without restraint. The season's totals would show that man reduced the total rainfall by his efforts.

Of course, nature does not always run through the complete cycle from cloud *A* to cloud *G*. On any given day, depending upon the moisture availability and the amount of insolation, cloud *G* may never be formed. If, on such a day, the cloud seeder touches off a cloud of size *E* or *F*, he has really done a job: generated rain where none would have fallen but for his efforts.

It does not surprise me that the results of controlled seeding experiments go first one way and then the other. The lesson I learn, however, is that seeding experiments designed just to knock off a few clouds are destined to failure. If the aim is rainmaking, we must learn how to build clouds, probably relying on nature to handle their destruction. What we must learn to do, I think, involves building several clouds of size *G* in the same place on any specific day. If we can do that, then unquestionably the amount of precipitation can be increased. Our efforts could then no longer be described as a matter of displacing a rain shower, giving Farmer Brown the rain nature intended to give to Farmer Smith down the road.

Is there any possibility that we can force feed clouds? I think there is. In explaining, however, I find it necessary to backtrack to the period when I, too, joined the ranks of cloudbusters, intent only on dissipating a single cloud in the sky.

The theory of rain development in middle latitudes has been generally accepted. Unless an ice phase is involved, there is no significant precipitation. In the tropics, it is a different story. There, a great deal of rain falls from clouds that never grow tall enough to reach the very high level of the freezing isotherm in the tropical atmosphere. The mechanism by which rain forms in such clouds has been very puzzling to atmospheric scientists. Obviously, there must be some other explanation for the way that tiny cloud droplets coalesce or otherwise combine into the necessary few large drops.

Of course, it is not really the ice phase that is essential. Ice is only a means to an end. The key requirement is a number of large drops of water in an otherwise stable cloud. This fact was well-established by an Australian investigator, E. G. Bowen, who set clouds off just by dumping water from an airplane tanker into their centers.

The most widely accepted hypothesis now, for explaining tropical rain, calls for the presence of giant condensation nuclei in the atmosphere. Relatively large salt crystals, for example, when serving as nuclei for water-vapor condensation, would, by their own bulk, produce droplets considerably larger than the usual 8/10,000 inch size.

I cannot gainsay this hypothesis. Some or all tropical rain may well be produced in just this way. I do have another hypothesis, however, that I think will also serve to explain tropical rainfall. It involves, as does the ice phase theory, differences in vapor pressures.

In the ice mechanism, when the temperature is about 5°F (−15°C), the rate at which water molecules leave a liquid surface can be represented by the number 1.436. At the same temperature, the rate of evaporation (sublimation) from ice is given by the number 1.241; the difference is obviously 0.195. (For those who are interested, the numbers are the vapor pressures, in millimeters of mercury over ice and over water.) Apparently, this difference is sufficient to provide distillation from the surface with the greater rate of evaporation to the surface with the smaller rate.

Examination of the rates of evaporation of liquid water as a function of temperature shows one relevant feature. As the temperature rises, the rate of evaporation goes up, too—not uniformly, but at an accelerated pace. Close to the freezing temperature, for example, the difference in rates for a couple

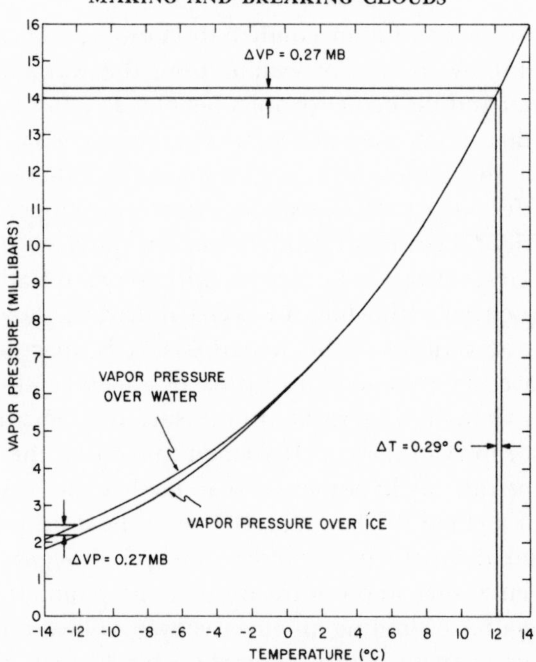

Vapor Pressure over Ice and Water

of tenths of a degree is only 0.068. Close to the boiling point of water, the difference per 0.2° is 5.42. At the probable temperature of clouds in the tropics, the difference is 0.218. This value is very close to the difference between ice and water, which is said to account for midlatitude rain.

It seemed to me that it was not unreasonable to attribute tropical rain to a slight difference in temperature between neighboring cloud droplets. Suppose one droplet was carried upward from the bottom of the cloud while its neighbor of the moment originated high in the cloud but was swept down in a downdraft. Might not the first droplet have a temperature of 20.2°C while the second had a temperature of 20°C? If this were so, I would expect some evaporation from the warmer droplet and some condensation on the cooler one. Of course, just by the act of evaporation, the warmer droplet would cool and the cooler droplet heat up as water condensed on it so that the process in a static atmosphere would quickly stop. But the atmosphere is not static, and there must be many different droplets of slightly different temperatures in it that might, because of random motion, produce the requisite few larger droplets needed to initiate precipitation.

The question with which I was confronted was how to demonstrate the validity of this hypothesis. It is difficult enough to measure the average temperature of a mass of cloud droplets; it is virtually impossible to measure the temperature of a single droplet in the sky. It seemed to me that the best way to demonstrate my hypothesis was to modify the temperature of part of a cloud deliberately. If I could heat up part of the cloud and dissipate it (produce rain?), I thought I would have taken a long step toward proving my point. It then became a matter of finding an effective way to heat a cloud.

For this purpose, I selected carbon black—soot, the ultrafine powder that collects on the chimney of a kerosene lamp and which is manufactured commercially by the incomplete combustion of natural gas. Why carbon black? For several reasons, but the primary one was that soot is the blackest substance known to man. It reflects almost no light. It is more than 99 per cent efficient in trapping every bit of light energy falling upon it. And since this energy is trapped, it heats the carbon. For the same reason that one does not wear dark clothes on a hot summer's day, for the same reason that men in polar regions are careful not to drop oil or tar on an ice runway lest they create pot holes, carbon black picks up heat and gets hot.

Calculations show that theoretically, at least, a pound of very finely divided carbon scattered in the bright sunshine in such a way that each particle is fully exposed, could pick up enough energy each minute to raise the temperature of eleven tons of water from the freezing point to the boiling point. Practically, of course, no such tremendous quantity of heat can be attained. There is shadowing and clumping and the efficiency is reduced enormously. Nonetheless, the amount of heating is probably still considerable and presumably quite sufficient to heat a section of cloud. In a cloud, of course, the carbon is not really exposed to direct sunlight, but it is quite light even in the interior of a cloud, and it is not just the top surface of the carbon particle that is exposed. Reflections from water droplets illuminate the entire surface so that the heating efficiency is not substantially reduced by shielding from direct sunlight. Other reasons for the choice of carbon black included its availability, its cheapness, and its complete lack of toxicity.

The idea, then, was to drop a small quantity of finely powdered carbon into a cloud and depend upon the development of a difference in temperature between the water droplets to produce the requisite number of larger globules of water.

The Navy let me use one of the Hurricane Hunters—a superb aircraft modified from the Superconstellation of commercial use—to make the carbon runs on the clouds and assigned several photo reconnaissance planes to record the results. Any experimentation involving aircraft is, of course, fantastically expensive, but except for air time, which could justifiably be charged to crew training, the initial carbon-black experiments were so simple and so inexpensive as to be almost unbelievable.

A short length of stovepipe, costing $1.69, was inserted into a small hatch in the bottom of the plane. Approximately $3.00 worth of carbon was wrapped into one-pound packages, using ordinary wrapping paper secured by transparent tape to which a six-foot length of nylon cord was fastened. The idea was to secure the other end of the cord to a convenient stanchion in the plane and drop the package down the chute. As

Dissipation of a Cloud Using Carbon Black. Pictures Taken at

One Minute after Carboning

Five Minutes after Carboning

Different Angles but Treated Cloud Is Outlined on Each Picture.

Three Minutes after Carboning

Eight Minutes after Carboning

it reached the end of its tether, the tape would be jerked off and the package opened in the slipstream of the plane.

We took off from Naval Air Station Jacksonville, Florida, flew out over the ocean and selected a cloud. It was actively growing from a base at about 2,500 feet to a top at about 11,000 feet. The edges were crisp and sharp; the turrets looked like boiling cauldrons, stretching upward another thousand feet or so. Into the cloud we flew, throwing a one-pound package of carbon through the stovepipe as we exchanged the bright sunlight for the white glare of the cloud's interior. Minutes of frustration followed. With several other aircraft about, for safety's sake, the Superconnie had to hold its course, and we could not see the treated cloud. We had to depend upon the observer photographic planes to tell us what was going on.

For long minutes we heard nothing. Then suddenly, the air came alive with ejaculations. I know of no way to translate the excitement that came through amid the crackle and static of the plane's radio receivers. Only because all communications were recorded and I can rerun the tapes am I able to reconstruct at all the mixture of disbelief, wonder, and amazement which constituted the observers' reaction. Motion pictures and stills preserving the visual evidence help bolster my feeling of having been present at a miraculous tour de force.

The observers reported that after several minutes during which nothing happened, the cloud suddenly spurted upward from a point just above our flight level. A tunnel formed where we had flown through the cloud, opening and widening rapidly until the cloud was sliced in two. The upper section darted up several thousand feet, becoming very wispy and transparent. Moments after its push upwards, it thinned out and then it was gone. Almost simultaneously, the bottom half of the cloud turned very dark and, as though a giant had wiped a sponge over a slate, it, too, disappeared. The observers were unanimous in testifying that there was nothing gradual about the process. "Now you see it. Now you don't!" the pilot of a jet plane flying toward the cloud reported. The others agreed.

During the next several days, we attacked a number of other clouds in the same way, achieving very much the same result. We realized, of course, that we were not proving anything since no controls were run. It would have been necessary for us to fly through some of the clouds without dispersing carbon to insure that it was not the effect of the airplane itself or some other factor that was responsible for what we saw. We had only a few days to perform our demonstration and enough controlled experiments to be valid statistically could not be concentrated into such a short period of time.

But we were excited! In the evening, we speculated on what was going on in the clouds: Why the separation, the thinning out to nothingness of the top and the darkening and erasure of the bottom. It seemed to me that everything could be explained by our having introduced heat into the cloud. When one heats a fluid mass from below, one decreases its stability and starts the fluid churning upwards. The upper part of the cloud was being heated from below by the carbon we had introduced. Obeying the proper physical laws, the air was pushed up by surrounding cooler air. Since there was no source of water vapor at the 7,000-8,000 foot level where we carboned, the droplets spread out and evaporated into the dry air above.

The lower part of the cloud, we were heating from above. The heated layer served as a lid or cover for the lower part of the cloud and prevented moisture-laden air from penetrating higher. In addition, the temperature difference, I thought, would result in the distillation of water from the warmer to the cooler droplets producing a growth in drop size. This increase in size would explain the darkening of the cloud. I guessed that the bottom of the cloud disappeared because the large drops simply fell out.

Between night and morning, we dreamed up an experiment which might indicate whether some part of my hypothesis was correct. If we were in fact supplying heat to a layer of air and if this was sufficient to lift a considerable mass, we should be able to generate a cloud where one did not exist earlier. If we heated a humid but cloudless sample of air, we should be able to raise it to a level where condensation would take place.

Early one morning when the sky was clear of clouds for a distance of at least twenty-five miles, we flew a carefully laid track between two easily recognizable landmarks. At a low level in the clear air, we dribbled out five pounds of carbon suspended in five gallons of water. Using a stop watch and knowledge of the plane's speed, we poured out the mixture for a distance of one mile. Turning in a large circle, we flew back parallel to our track and then back again. A straight, mile-long row of clouds developed in the sky as we watched.

In the same way that one swallow does not make a summer, one apparent success does not prove a hypothesis. When I was forced to return to Washington because I was needed (?) there and the planes were needed elsewhere, I had proved nothing, but, to the extent that I could separate a non-scientific part of me from a scientific part, I was sure that I had a tool for performing significant work in weather modification.

Although I still believe this to be essentially true, my original thoughts were in error. I was still thinking of knocking off clouds. It was this aspect which intrigued me most. Now, I think that the cloud generation was the most important part of the demonstration. By using an artificial source of heat—be it carbon or some other means—it should be possible to generate clouds and to build them up by repeated

Man-made Clouds

heat injections until they are large enough to rain out. It should be possible to do this faster and more often than nature will do it as long as there is a source of moist air available.

By one of those freak actions of fate, my hypothesis has never been tested properly. Fate took the guise of politics. One of the states was suffering a severe drought shortly after my return to Washington. Over my very vociferous protests, a team was drafted with me as head, to "make it rain." We did, too. The wind shifted just at the time our transport plane with its cartons of carbon and its crates of jury-rigged dispensing equipment landed on the runway in the drought area. We deplaned and unpacked in the rain. And it rained every day we were there, the wind and weather shifting again when we finally left for Washington in disgust.

During the first several days of our stay, our little party was hailed as saviors by the local citizenry who gathered at the restaurants and motels we frequented. As the rains continued, more and more people asked us politely but pointedly when we were thinking of going home. Enough was obviously enough.

A few must still have felt that they had been cheated since we would frequently find little notes at our operations office: "It has not yet rained on my farm. Please do something about it. You can find it by following the main road north for 6.2 miles (to the Baptist Church with the white spire) and turning left for $\frac{6}{10}$ mile. Thank you."

We disclaimed all responsibility for the rain but succeeded only in getting marks for modesty. One of the leading newspapers, on its front page, proclaimed "Scientist Refuses to Take Credit for the Rain."

Needless to say, we accomplished nothing scientifically and managed to disgust ourselves and many of the scientific community by this exercise, although most understood that we had had no choice. The net result was entirely negative. An aura of charlatanism hung over our work and by the time this had dissipated, the move was on to take weather modification back to the laboratory. Whatever support we received later to reinstitute a scientific research project came from those who had their own axes to grind. As a result, our plans served mainly as a portmanteau for schemes of others and became so disfigured as to lose all resemblance to a scientific program designed to find an answer to the question of whether modification is possible. All such proposals floundered under their own weight.

13
Goals and Dreams

To make progress in any field, one must dream: considering some aspect of the world as it is now and imagining how it might be. Whether it is a Columbus dreaming of commerce between the East Indies and the old world, a Robert Fulton envisaging ships traveling without concern for the vagaries of the wind, a Richard E. Byrd pioneering a new continent with vast resources hidden under its mountains of snow and ice, or a Werner von Braun anticipating the revelation of what have been heretofore mysteries of the universe, visions of the future are as necessary ingredients to research as laboratories, technicians, and money.

Although the scientist is a dreamer, he is no Walter Mitty —not if he is a good scientist. His visions are controlled by facts and by the possible. He curbs and checks his dreams until they represent realistic programs for future work and he continually evaluates and re-evaluates them not only in the light of his own discipline, not only with respect to interactions with other disciplines, but also, if he is a responsible scientist, in terms of world views, present and future.

Nowhere is realistic dreaming more necessary than in weather control. In no field is there more of a requirement to enlarge the field of vision from the narrow objective of specific accomplishment to the greater horizons of global values.

The most simple illustration will serve to exemplify this point. For centuries, the Hollanders have been pushing back the sea in order to create more terrain for agricultural purposes. Within recent years, the Zuider Zee has been closed off and a new lake created, the Ijsel Meer. Much of the water was drained out into the North Sea and numbers of new farm communities created. How imaginative and creative all this seems. And it is. But the ecology of insect life has been altered by this changed balance between land and water. A ruinous insect population grew out of all proportion because, presumably, some restraint on its development was removed by the Hollanders' changing of the face of their little corner of the world. Stringent measures had to be taken to save the crops, and while, at last report, this scourge is under control, an ecological balance has probably not yet been achieved. The stringent measures, in turn, disturb the environment in their own way. Like a pebble thrown into a pond, the ripples extend outward in everwidening circles. Unlike the pebble in the pond, any single ripple can suddenly develop into a tidal wave if conditions are just right.

We dream of weather control, but along with our efforts to achieve it, we must take a hard-headed look at all that it will entail. Let us take a goal which is not too different from that sought by the Netherlanders. Instead of reclaiming land from the sea, many of us would like to reclaim desert land, increasing the agricultural productivity by bringing water to arid areas. We know that the soil, uncultivated through the centuries, is fertile. All it needs is a little water in order to convert the Mojave or the Sahara into rich gardens that will help feed the world. And this can be done—not right now, perhaps, but when the economic pressures of the population explosion channel man's time and money into the research to achieve this weather-control goal.

But what happens when the atmosphere is forced to carry moisture to desert areas, there to release its cargo in the form of rain? Where did the water come from? Where was it going and where would it have been released if we had not forced the atmosphere into an unnatural pattern? Not only must the effects, immediate and long range, of this diversion of water be studied but also another category of effect. The desert areas in the southwest of the United States, hot and sunbaked, are almost always dominated by a heat low. The low-pressure system over that region is almost a permanent feature of any weather map of the United States. If rain is brought to the desert there, the vegetation and the clouds will change the area from one that reflects much of the heat energy it receives to one that retains the heat. The "permanent" heat low will no longer be present. It is quite conceivable that the entire weather picture of the United States could be changed as a result and that the over-all climatic regimes in the plain states or New England could be significantly modified.

If one segment of our scientific community is engaged in converting a desert into one continuous oasis, another segment would do well to be studying what the long-range effects will be—long range in terms of time as well as in terms of downstream effects. And it is not only the meteorologist who must give this attention. Entomologists, geologists, economists, and many others must study the resultant problems.

A tropical rain belt girds the earth near the equator where little that is economically valuable grows and where scattered natives live a primitive existence, requiring almost nothing in the way of shelter or clothing for comfort and survival. Perhaps we could modify that climate, making it more fruitful and closer to our own norms for residence. Again, we must consider not only the effect of this effort on the lower forms of life: plants, insects, small animals, but also the effect on the large animals which live there, including particularly the most developed animal of all—man. Presumably, the native population will explode with the improved climate but so will the requirements for less primitive shelter and more than rudimentary clothing.

These types of weather control may be quite far in the future, and perhaps need not necessarily concern us now, although I think they should. Let us consider another type in which active research is now being conducted. The Navy and the Weather Bureau together are engaged in Project Stormfury, an effort to modify and control hurricanes. For the past several years, they have been flying into or over hurricanes, dispersing large quantities of silver iodide into the wall clouds in an attempt to reduce the severity or change the course of the giant storms. Parenthetically, it should be noted that what they are doing is a heat-control experiment. While the silver iodide converts liquid-water droplets to ice, it is not the ice crystal that they are interested in. What concerns them is that for every pound of water they change to ice, they release more than 36,000 calories in a limited section of the storm. This is roughly enough heat to raise the temperature of 13 ounces of liquid water from the freezing point to the boiling point. (Plug: Look up the effect of carbon black.)

A fairly considerable body of knowledge about cloud behavior and heat utilization is being acquired as a result of this project but, in my opinion, it is a dead-end project, a fact I find very comforting. While the reasons for both my pessimism and for my finding solace in pessimism should be noted, let me discuss the latter first since it follows directly the cautionary point of view expressed earlier concerning ecological effects. Fundamentally, the function of "weather" is to achieve a balance between the extremes of conditions prevailing in the tropics and at the poles. Perhaps more important than all the individual outbursts of cold and warm air following the various frontal passages in bringing some measure of equalization is the occasional hurricane or typhoon. The energy transported across the latitudinal divisions by these tropical giants during their week or more of life defies description. From their birth just off the equator to their death often in latitude 50° or 60°, they carry fantastic quantities of water and latent heat poleward. Even after their official demise, when winds have dropped below the requisite 75 miles per hour, which earns them their name, they survive as great extratropical cyclones encompassing areas as large as half a continent.

No one knows at this time whether these tropical giants play an essential function in maintaining a reasonable circulation between poles and equator. Before a means is found to prevent their formation or to kill them in infancy, however, an answer should be found. It is not inconceivable that if they are consistently prevented from carrying out their unconscious mission, a disastrous state of unbalance might be created. Perhaps a superhurricane would eventually result that would make the presently known hurricane look like a pygmy. Perhaps a less dramatic but equally devastating world-wide climate change would result.

It is considerations like these that enable me to feel good about the probable lack of success of hurricane modification experiments. Since the researchers will probably not soon learn how to control these giant storms, there is time for the necessary back-up studies to take place.

And why will the means to control hurricanes not be found soon? For two reasons. First, the weapons available to attack the atmosphere are still puny indeed. We cannot effectively handle a volume one-hundredth the size of the hurricane or one possessing one-thousandth of its energy. Eventually, we may learn how—not only by developing better weapons but also by learning where to apply them. But the time does not seem to be now.

The second reason is closely related to the first. We are not likely to develop better hurricane-modification tools because we do not know what we are accomplishing. Over and over again in scientific methodology, the emphasis is placed upon control experiments. The scientist must always know what would have happened had he not interfered with a specific process before he can determine whether his interference produced any effect.

The problem is that there are so few hurricanes annually and so few of them are suitable for experimentation since, with commendable caution, stringent rules have been laid down as to the area in which modification experiments may be conducted. Only if a hurricane is well away from populated areas may experimentation take place. So there are very few hurricanes to work with, and hurricanes are noted for their eccentricity. There is no possible change in path following a modification experiment that cannot be matched by an undisturbed hurricane. Does a hurricane suddenly decay or intensify or break into two storms? Instances of these occurrences abound in tropical-storm literature. Hurricane Betsy of September 1965 affords the perfect example. She developed slowly, far out at sea, and for days the newspapers carried articles about the plans for seeding her. Then she accelerated and moved into an area where the established rules forbade seeding operations, and the experiment was cancelled. Shortly after, Betsy turned in her tracks, abandoned her apparent assault on the Carolina coast and headed for Florida. Miami, the Florida Keys, Mississippi, and Louisiana suffered the fury of the most vicious hurricane of this century. What relief those directing Project Stormfury must have felt that they had not touched that storm. Would they have been blamed for all the destruction she left in her wake? Would they have believed themselves responsible for her odd behavior?

No, it is not likely that much will be accomplished in the

field of hurricane control, or, if it is, that the man-made effects will be recognized. Fortunately, however, the by-products of this experimentation are valuable, contributing significant additions to scientific knowledge of atmospheric configurations.

The orderly way of proceeding, it seems to me, is not by attacking the greatest and most eccentric of atmospheric phenomena but to start at the other end of the scale with the smallest and most reproducible.

Another restriction on the types of weather-control activities follows from the precautions listed earlier. Since we do not really know what the long-range effects of experimental actions may be, it behooves those performing research in the atmosphere to insure that they produce no permanent changes.

Any material introduced into the lowest 40,000 feet or so of the atmosphere will persist for only a limited time. Within a matter of days at most, the atmosphere will cleanse itself of contaminants and, if desired, a complete return to the original status can be achieved. The introduction of contaminants into the upper atmosphere or into space is something else again. Some have suggested that a layer of reflective material be dispersed between the sun and earth to change the amount of solar energy reaching the earth. Others recommend the use of an absorptive material. And there are other suggestions of material which could be dispersed from a satellite. I can only plead that if any substance must be introduced into space or near-space, that whatever is used be short-lived. An immediate beneficial effect can easily be followed by a long-term deleterious one.

With the air cleared by these notes of sagacity and wisdom, we can now continue dreaming on our own. What is the logical approach to securing a weather-control capability for us at some time in the foreseeable future?

A list of some of the objectives should be compiled so that

each can be discussed in turn:

a. Bring rain to certain desert areas.
b. Eliminate or reduce the severity or frequency of destructive concommitants of thunderstorms—hail, lightning, tornadoes.
c. Bring rain to drought-stricken areas (distinct from desert areas).
d. Over limited areas, control fog and smog.
e. Steer midlatitude cyclones that dump unwanted and crippling quantities of snow and rain on urban areas.
f. Steer or otherwise control hurricanes and typhoons.

Come the millenium! What a formidable list of goals. More or less they have been listed in what I consider to be the order in which they can be accomplished with the more easily achievable first.

If the control of heat is really the prod we can use to force the atmosphere to do our bidding, experimentation must first be performed in developing the means of introducing (or removing) controlled quantities of heat into the atmosphere. To develop this tool, it would probably be well to experiment with the small cumulus clouds of the summer day. They could serve as the guinea pigs needed in two ways. First, they themselves are yardsticks to show the effectiveness of a given heat source. If you applied heat below one of them and made it grow significantly larger than its neighbors, you would know that you had done a job. The relative effectiveness of various sources of heat could be tested directly in this way.

Perhaps a more significant test procedure would involve using a tracer material. The size of the area that nourishes an undisturbed cloud, giving it moisture, could be determined by distributing tracer material in the air outside the cloud and sampling inside at a later time to see whether the tracer material had reached it. Once the feeding area of a natural cloud was determined, the effect of various heating procedures on the area could be found.

As a side note, a few words about such a tracer technique might be interesting. Obviously, the tracer material will be present in the cloud in almost infinitesimal quantities. If an airplane were to fly through the cloud trying to collect tracer on filter paper, for example, it would be very difficult to collect enough for chemical analysis. If the tracer were radioactive, it would be far simpler, since the most minute quantities of radioactive materials can be measured using geiger counters or other detection means.

There is a problem, however, about using radioactive tracers. No one wants radioactive materials in the atmosphere. Quite justifiably, everyone wants to minimize exposure to radioactive contaminants. Scientists have been developing a tracer that is completely inert but which can be made radioactive. This material in its inert form can be introduced into the atmosphere. It can be caught on filters in its inert form and brought back to the laboratory. There, it can be placed in an atomic reactor, made radioactive, and its concentration measured. They are encountering a number of problems in this development so that this tracer tool cannot yet be said to be ready for use. The technique is so ingenious and would prove to be so useful that one can only hope they will soon succeed in overcoming the various problems.

With this experimentation on forced cloud development, there might easily be a valuable by-product: rainfall over areas with summertime cumulus clouds might be increased. During the last several years, while the East Coast of the United States has been suffering serious and prolonged drought conditions, such experimentation might have proved very valuable.

To continue our discussion of ways of achieving weather control, let us assume that we have developed the means for using heat as a workable tool. Many desert areas are reasonably close to a limitless source of water supply but are separated from it by a high coastal range of mountains which prevents the moist maritime air from reaching the arid land. An onshore breeze carries the water vapor inland on the coastal plain, but then the air is pushed upward as it reaches the mountains. As it rises, it cools, ice crystals are formed, and it rains—rains on the windward side so that when the mountain range is scaled, the water has been wrung out of the cloud and dry air descends on the leeward side.

If some part of the cooling on the windward side could be counteracted as the moist air ascends, it might be possible to prevent complete rain-out there so that moist air could flow to the arid regions beyond. A judicious amount of heat introduced prior to or during the ascent might do the job. It would be necessary to control the heat because too much would just intensify the effect we desire to counteract. If too much were introduced, the cloud would go surging upward to rain out even without the influence of the mountain range.

Once moist air was available over the desert, techniques could be found to make it deposit its water if nature did not do the job by itself.

For performing this type of experimentation, I would not recommend working with mountain ranges. I would suggest a much more modest approach using a single mountain as my test subject. There are a number of more or less isolated mountains that are characterized during the summer months by a cloud cap. Each day, a cloud develops over the mountain peak, often generating a downwind thunderstorm as the day ages. The experiment would involve trying to prevent that orographic cloud from forming. Presumably, if that could be done, the same technique could be extended to a range of mountains.

Having disposed of one of our goals or, more correctly, having reached stage one in our dreams for the future, let us dream some more—about ways to eliminate some of the destructiveness of thunderstorm-related phenomena. It is the giant thunderstorm that produces the damage. Thus, the logical approach to this problem would seem to be to keep thunderstorms small.

Two possible techniques seem feasible: either a man-made ceiling could be imposed on a developing thunderstorm or a competing circulation established so that the energy inherent in a single storm would be spread through several.

It would seem possible to establish some sort of thunderstorm patrol. Aircraft at a very high altitude could survey tremendous areas of land below so that relatively few planes would be required to monitor the skies during a period when the Weather Bureau predicted the possibility of violent thunderstorms—their "Black Area" forecast. These planes would watch the development of thunderstorms and would guide a "seeding" plane to any which threatened to exceed some arbitrary ceiling: say 30,000 feet. By heating the air above such a burgeoning thunderstorm, it might be possible to stabilize it and cut off some of its energy. Another possibility would entail deliberately generating a competing storm near it to draw away some of the moisture or updraft. If such a method were physically practical, it would also be economically feasible. The cost in loss of life and property resulting from any one of these giant thunderstorms would be far larger than the funds required to keep a limited number of airplanes on guard duty during the relatively infrequent and short periods of tornado alert.

In the effort to steer cyclones, both tropical and extratropical, similar techniques can perhaps be found to modify the circulation by applying heat energy in vulnerable parts of the storms. The emphasis here would be to know enough about the storm to be able to trigger a reaction. It does not seem reasonable to assume that the amount of energy that can be introduced artificially would be enough to do any significant amount of work by itself. The energy of the existing storm would have to be relied upon to exert the major effort. The introduction of the man-made stimulus would merely channel the power of the storm properly and make it useful.

Pipe dreams? Indeed! Much as these suggestions may have sounded like programs for action, they are, at this point, only untried ideas. They are dreams—the type of dreams which sustain those who strive for achievement beyond the realm of present-day capability: exploring the stars, farming the ocean, controlling the weather. Dreams, yes, but such as originate in the fertile mind of man as creator, not such as those which flicker in the smoke of a pipe of opium.

14

Meteorology Must Grow Up

What of the future? Weather control is a bright, though as yet unrealized, hope for future years. Presumably, all agree that much further research is needed to make this dream a realization. Surely, we can also agree that much more work must be done to improve weather forecasts.

I will give hearty support to all valid efforts to improve the accuracy with which we can foretell what the weather will be at some future time whether it be hours, days, or weeks ahead, but I would also suggest that before much progress can be made, a better job of public relations and public education is required. What the average citizen expects from those who forecast his weather he cannot really get, and there seems little possibility that he will ever get it. Unfortunately, those concerned with the forecasting problem have never informed the public of this impossibility and have not sought to make them understand the situation. Let me explain.

We have mentioned the little box on the front page of the newspaper that gives the weather forecast. John Q. Public thinks this should be gospel, knows that it is not, and feels offended when the information it gives is incorrect. In the same newspaper, somewhere on the back pages, there is usually a column discussing health problems. While the former is read with the conviction that it should be completely accurate, the latter is read for general interest. In the case of actual illness, the reader does not accept the words of the doctor-columnist, he goes to his physician for more accurate or at least more pertinent information.

His symptoms are analyzed, his condition diagnosed, and treatment is prescribed. Then he is given a medical forecast but the doctor is more canny than the weatherman. If the patient is suffering from flu or some other virus-produced respiratory ailment, along with his drugs he receives the assurance that it will probably clear up in a few days or a week. He is not told that he will be well at 4 P.M. on Thursday next.

If his physical condition requires surgery, he is not told specifically that he will live or die, but rather, in the discussion, it will be said or implied, that only a small fraction of a percent of patients succumb to that particular surgical procedure. On the other hand, for a serious operation, the patient or his relatives, may be warned of the considerable risk involved. Further, even with an incurable disease, no medical doctor can state specifically the life expectancy of a patient and few even try. Is there anyone who does not know of an individual still walking around years after being told by a rash physician that he had only six months to live?

When there are as many variables as there are in the human body and the human spirit or as there are in the interaction of the earth, the sun, the ocean, and the atmosphere, it is foolhardy to give absolute statements about the course of future events and just as foolhardy to accept them. The logical approach, I think, is to state the probabilities of the various events which may occur. In some circumstances, the probabilities are so high as to amount to virtual certainty. In others, one of two or more things may happen and the probability of each given a percentage value. In brain surgery, perhaps, for a given operation there may be a 20 per cent chance that the patient will die, a 45 per cent chance that he will survive and be badly crippled, and a 35 per cent chance that he will recover entirely.

In weather forecasting, there may be a 65 per cent chance that a front will pass during the next twenty-four hours and that the weather will turn cool while there is still 35 per cent probability that the front will lag and that the hot, humid weather will linger on. The weather forecaster is not permitted to make such a statement, however; 50 per cent is a sort of magic number for him. If the percentage creeps past that boundary, he must forecast the event. If it remains less than 50 per cent, he forecasts that the event will not occur. The odds are badly stacked against him.

If the public would understand and accept a probability forecast, it would not be cheated. Suppose a family picnic were planned. Either consciously or unconsciously, the planner assigns probability values to many significant factors other than weather. Will little Suzy be over her cold before Sunday? Will the family car be in operating condition? Will a crisis develop at the office so that Daddy will have to work on Sunday? Will Uncle Joe and Aunt May select this weekend for their annual visit? The probability of any one or more of these events occurring covers the range between high and low. The prospective picnic planner takes them in stride and knows that the picnic may or may not come off as planned. If weather were thrown into this list as, for example, "80 per cent chance of good picnic weather," surely the planning of the picnic would not be made more difficult.

If the public would accept a probability forecast in weather as they accept it in almost any other area of human endeavor, the forecaster would be free to concentrate his efforts on doing the job he has been trained to do: evaluate the various possible sequences of weather events, assigning each a considered confidence value. His work and his research could then be more meaningful and rewarding because his objective would be realistic.

Another avenue for the improvement of weather science also involves not only the meteorologist but also many other individuals. The public, the scientific community, and the meteorologists alike must recognize that meteorology is just one subbranch of physics. It is true that at one time meteorology was an art and that a combination of interest, corns, and rheumatism enabled almost anyone to practise weather forecasting. But then, after all, for many years the local barber was the surgeon of the medical profession and grandmother concocted her own tonics, poultices, and noxious nostrums. The time of home medicine and amateur weathermen is long past. Meteorology, like medicine, is evolving into a science and must join the fraternity of science. Biologists, endocrinologists, geneticists, chemists, metallurgists, all contribute to the practice of medical science. The same need for interdisciplinary exchange exists in weather science. Only if all contribute to the developments in atmospheric physics can it be properly furthered, and only if a physicist dealing with the atmosphere as a specialty is free to move to another specialty without prejudice can weather science attract the finest talent. How many bright young men and women care to put themselves on a dead-end street professionally: meteorology and Weather Bureau employment—or nothing?

Much to the shame of the profession, statistics reveal that meteorologists collectively have fewer university degrees and smaller annual incomes than almost all other scientific groups. Unless the professional level and the remuneration are raised, there can be little hope for progress.

Crucial to future progress in mastery of the atmosphere is the matter of money for weather operations and weather research. To me it seems that the level of financial support—the bite these pursuits take out of the national budget—is adequate, although I suppose no one should ever confess this. One of the major problems, however, is the question of emphasis—how this money is used. A considerable part of it does not seem used to greatest advantage. Congress, quite properly, plays the role of watchdog on the expenditure of these funds and constantly tries to insure that there will be no duplication in the efforts exerted by the Weather Bureau, the National Aeronautics and Space Agency, the Military Services, the Departments of Agriculture and Interior, the Atomic Energy Commission, to name only a few of the agencies involved in weather studies.

As one who has both watched and been involved for many years in the various gyrations on the duplication issue, I have always been amazed at the complete inability of legislators to come to grips with the question of what is duplication and what is not. (Of course, they get little help from those directly involved.) Somehow, however, they always manage to cry "duplication and waste" at those features where duplication is not only justifiable but also valuable and miss entirely the areas where wasteful practices are actually occurring.

A great deal of this confusion exists because meteorological thinking has not kept pace with meteorological technical advances so that those in the profession have no clear idea of how the various functions and responsibilities should be allocated. Without a clear picture, it is impossible to assess duplication and waste with any degree of reason. The trouble stems from the time-honored manner in which meteorology operates. Certain procedures have been followed since time immemorial and, by and large, the new scientific tools are being used to permit going through these same procedures more easily, more quickly, and more accurately.

A medical analogy may again be appropriate. There was a time when a single doctor acted as an independent unit. He examined, diagnosed, prescribed, and then filled the prescription from his own pharmacy. If the medical profession had followed the example of the meteorologists, the individual doctor would be equipped with his own x-ray laboratory, pathology laboratory, surgery, hospital, and have a storeroom full of every drug prepared by the prolific pharmaceutical industry. The modern doctor does not operate in this way, of course. He does the work for which he is best qualified and uses the specialized abilities of others to insure the maximum benefit to his patients. Meteorology has not yet made this transition. The entire science should take a tremendous stride forward when those working in it, those directing it, and those controlling its purse strings come to grips with the revolutionary thought that the new technology should alter the philosophy of meteorological operations.

Even local jurisdictions, city, county, and state, must get involved in furthering meteorological progress. Much like the youngster who confessed that "he didn't believe in ghosts but that he was afraid of them," many local governments have passed statutes outlawing atmospheric experimentation, particularly weather modification, within their boundaries. Certainly, uncontrolled and irresponsible experimentation should be made illegal, but blanket taboos can only stifle all possibility of progress.

Obviously, I am able to continue at great length on the subject of what is wrong with my profession and with its reception by the world at large, but I will observe proper restraint and confine myself to one final suggestion. The exploration and exploitation of outer space is important to us all. So is the exploration and exploitation of inner space—the oceans—that lately have occupied so much attention. I venture to guess, however, that the exploration and exploitation of the space in which we all live and work and play is not less important than either of these. Let us get on with our job. Weather or not!

Index

Air, *see* Atmosphere
Air Force, U.S., 32, 70, 143
  Strategic Air Command, 53-54
Aircraft carriers
  Enterprise's raid, 1-10, 11
  limitations on attacks from, 13-14
  after Pearl Harbor, 3-4
  sinking of, 12
  take-offs and landings on, 14-16
Airplanes
  distinguished by radar from clouds, 35
  forecasting for, 135-37
  hazards from balloons to, 51-52
  identification of, 149-50
  landing aids for, 141-42
  tracking hurricanes with, 70-72, 218
Altocumulus clouds, 183, 185
Altostratus clouds, described, 183
Aneroid barometers, 177
"Angel Riding on the Yardarm," 13-16
Antitrades, 90-91
Arcata, Calif., 141-46
Arizona, U.S.S., 2-3
Armada, Spanish, 11
Army, U.S., 32
Aspre, 95
Atmosphere
  contamination of, 219
  factors influencing, 22-24
  weight and size of, 22
  See also Winds
Atmospheric pressure
  births and, 18
  deaths and, 18-19
  in hurricanes, 63
  measurement of, 176-80
  radiosonde observation of, 42-44
Atmospheric stability
  inversions and, 131-32
  mechanics of, 126-31
"Atmospherics," 164
Atomic bomb and weather, 77, 80
Austru, 95
Automatic weather stations, 24
  floating, 72-75

B-17 (airplane), 143
Balloons
  air-space violation by, 51, 53
  constant-altitude, 46-51
  as hazards to airplanes, 51-52
  soundings by, 40-44
  rockets dropped and fired from, 54

as UFO's, 51
Barometers
aneroid, 177
mercury, 176-80
Battleships sunk at Pearl Harbor, 2-3
Bermuda High, 91
Birds on radar, 29-30
Births, atmospheric pressure and, 18
Bjerknes, V., 102
Bowen, E. G., 202
Brandes, W. H., 102
Byrd, Rear Adm. Richard E., 213

California, U.S.S., 3
Canada, cold air mass of, 93, 116
Carbon-black seeding of clouds, 204-212
Carbon dioxide, temperature changes and, 85
Ceiling
defined, 40
determination of, 40-41
Ceilometer, 41
Central weather offices, reports from, 163-64
Charts, weather, *see* Maps
Chinook, 95-96
Circulation, *see* Winds
Cirrocumulus clouds, described, 182
Cirrostratus clouds, described, 182-83
Cirrus clouds, 65, 107
described, 181-82
Citrus growers, 189
Clear-air turbulence, 136
Climate
changes in, 76-87
weather control and, 189, 215
Clouds
formation of, 191-92
formation of rain in, 192-95
hurricane, 65
over islands, 130-31
man-made, 23-24, 210-11
orographic, 130, 222
radar echoes from, 28-37
seeding of, 196-212
author's carboning experiments, 204-12
suggested experiments with, 220-21
types of, 180-85
in weather lore, 106-8
Cold fronts, 116-21
described, 118-21
in escape of *Enterprise*, 7-9
formation of, 116-18
origin of, 5-7
on radar, 30-31
Condensation nuclei, 191-95, 202
Condensation trails, 23-24
Congress and expenditures for weather services, 229
Constant-altitude balloons, 46-51
Control of weather, 187-224
cloud-seeding in, 196-212
author's carboning experiments, 204-12
desert reclamation by, 214-15, 222
ecological problems of, 214-16
fog-seeding in, 196-97
hurricanes and, 216-19, 223-24
legal restrictions against, 230
logical approach to, 219-20
problem of satisfying everybody, 18
terminological problems in, 188-91
thunderstorms and, 223
Coral Sea, Battle of the, 12
Coriolis force, 6-7, 89
Crime rate, weather and, 18
Cumulonimbus clouds, 119, 183
described, 185
Cumulus clouds
described, 185
experiments with, 220
Cyclone, defined, 58

Deaths, atmospheric pressure and, 18-19
Deserts

instability over, 127
reclaiming, 214-15, 222
Dew, in weather lore, 108
DEW line, 113
Degree-days, 20
Doldrums, 90
Donora, Pa., 131
Dry ice, 196-97
Dust devils, 127

Earth's orbit, changes in, 86
Electric power plants, tailored forecasts for, 20
Electronic computers, 24, 158
maps produced by, 165
Enterprise, U.S.S., 1-10, 11
Eocene age, 81
Equatorial front, in Rabaul attacks, 14-16
Eye of hurricane, 61-62, 71-72

Facsimile-reproduced weather maps, 164, 165
Falkland Islands, Battle of, 11
Federal Aviation Agency, 113
Federal Communications Commission, 168
FIDO, 145-46
Floating automatic weather stations, 72-75
Flying saucers, balloons as, 51
Foehn wind, 95-100
Fog, 139-56
advection, 140-41
dispersion of, 145-47, 196-97
radiation, 105, 139-40
steam, 141
Folk sayings on weather, 104-9, 114-15
Forecasting
from central weather offices, 163-64
consumer orientation of, 134-37
difficulties of, 125-26
electronic computers in, 24, 158
in folk sayings, 104-9, 114-15
history of, 102-3
improving accuracy of, 225
in literature, 103-4
probability, 226-27
tailored, 19-21
Fossils, determination of past climate from, 81-83
Freezing level, radar detection of ("bright band"), 35-38
Freezing nuclei, 193-94
Frontolysis, 120
Fronts, 115-25
See also specific types of fronts
Frost, in weather lore, 108
Fulton, Robert, 213

Gilbert Islands, *Enterprise*'s raid on, 1-10, 11
Global circulation, 90-92
Goldbeater's skin, 138
"Greenhouse" effect, 85
Grocery store, weather and purchases from, 19
Ground Control Approach (GCA), 142
Guadalcanal, first landings on, 12-13
Guam, 66, 68

Hair in measurement of humidity, 138
Havre, Mont., 96
Haze in inversions, 132
History of weather science, 102-3
Holland, problems of land-building in, 214
Horse latitudes, 91
Humidity
measurement of, 137-39, 175
radiosonde observations of, 42-44
Hunold, Lt. Marguerite, 98-99
Hurricanes
control of, 216-19, 223-24
described, 60-65
detection of, 65-70
frequency of, 76, 78-80
girls' names for, 58-59

other terms for, 57
tracking of
airplanes, 70-72
floating stations, 72-75
radar, 72
satellites, 39

IFF (Identification: Friend or Foe), 149
Indian monsoon, 92-93
Infrared identification systems, 149-50, 154-55
Instability, *see* Atmospheric stability
Instrument Landing System (ILS), 142
Instrument shelters, 169-71
Instruments
primary vs. secondary, 177
See also Observations; *specific instruments*
Interior, Department of the, 190
International cooperation in weather, 157-59, 162
Intertropical front, in Rabaul attacks, 14-16
Inversions, 131-33
Irrigation ditches as weather modification, 190
Islands, clouds over, 130-31
Iso-echo contour radar, 32-35

Jacksonville, Fla., 208
Japanese Current, 140
Johnston Island, 69-70
Jutland, Battle of, 11

Katabatic circulation, 95
Klamath Falls, Ore., 98-99

Labrador Current, 140
Land, instable temperatures of, 89, 93
Land breeze, 94
Landing Aids Experimental Air Station, 141-46
Langmuir, Irving, 188
Lewes, Del., 151
Lexington, U.S.S., 12
Longuet-Higgins, Hugh Christopher, 68-70
Low-pressure centers, 58

Macelwane, Father J. B., 66-67
Maps, weather, 124-25
"canned," 164
cold fronts on, 30-31
computer-produced, 165
facsimile-reproduced, 164
first, 102
station data on, 161
upper-air, 44
Marshall Islands, *Enterprise*'s raid on, 1-10, 11
Maryland, U.S.S., 2
Medicine, weather and, 18-19
Mercury barometers, 176-80
Meteorology as profession and science, 228-30
Miami, Fla., 68, 69
Military Sea Transportation Service (MSTS), 167
Modification of weather
defined, 188-89
See also Control of weather
Monsoons, 92-93
Moon, in weather lore, 106-7
Moore, Charles B., 50-51
Mountain building and climatic changes, 84
Mountains, passage of air over, 130

Napoleon I, Emperor, 102
Navy, U.S., 70, 72, 113, 138
"airdales" vs. "black-shoe navy," 3
author's visit on PCE, 150-56
Fleet Weather Central Guam, 66
Landing Aids Experimental Station, 141-46
Naval Weather Service
author's cloud-seeding experi-

ment, 204-12
forecasts, 167-68
hurricane-control projects, 217
R. and D. section, 17, 25, 32
World War II historical studies, 10-17
Nevada, U.S.S., 3
New Haven, Conn., 78
New Testament, weather forecasting in, 103
Nimbostratus clouds, described, 184
NOMAD, 73-75
North pole, hypothesis of migration of, 83-84
Northern hemisphere, circulation in, 58

Observations
by airplanes, 161
of hurricanes, 70-72, 218
automatic, 24
floating stations, 72-75
of ceiling, 40-41
of clouds, 180-85
native, 125
of pressure, 176-80
of rainfall, 171-73
reporting network for, 159-64
by rocket, 45-46
of snowfall, 171
of temperature, 174-77
of winds
at ground stations, 173
by pilot balloons, 41-42
by radar on balloons, 163
reporting of, 173
Occluded fronts, 122-23
Ocean, *see* Sea
Oklahoma, U.S.S., 2
Oppau, Germany, 110
Orographic thunderstorms, 130, 222

Pearl Harbor, attack on, 2-4
Pilot balloon soundings (pibals), 41-42
PIREPS, 161
Polar air, *see* Cold fronts
Pressure, *see* Atmospheric pressure
Probability forecasts, 226-27
Proverbs, weather, 104-9, 114-15
Psychrometer (dry- and wet-bulb thermometers), 138, 175

Rabaul, air attacks on, 13-16
Radar
balloon soundings by, 42-44
bending of beams of, 113-14
measurement of refractive index, 137
described, 27-28
in Ground Control Approach, 142-43
weather echoes, 26-28
cold fronts, 30-31
freezing level ("bright band"), 35-38
hurricanes, 72, 73
thunderstorms, 31-36
in World War II, 25-26, 113
Radioactive-fallout forecasts, 164
Radioactive tracers in clouds, 221
Radioactivity, determination of, 191
Radiosonde, described, 42-44
Rain
formation of, 191-95
in tropics, 201-4
in hurricanes, 62
measurement of, 171-73
radar detection of, 28, 36-37
in weather lore, 106-9, 114-15
Rain gauges, 171-73
in rainmaking experiments, 198, 199
Rainbow, in weather lore, 106
Rainmaking, 188, 190-92, 196-212
See also Control of weather
Rapid City, S. Dak., 51
Rasonde, defined, 42
Rawin, defined, 42

Rawinsonde, defined, 42
Refractive index, measurement of, 137
Reporting of weather data, *see* Observations
Richard II (Shakespeare), 103, 104
Roaring Forties, 92
Rockets
  dropped and fired from balloons, 54
  weather soundings by, 45-46
Ross, Cmdr. Malcolm D., 51
Russell, Charles M., "Waiting for a Chinook," 96, 97
Russian-American weather interchange, 158-59

Salamis, Battle of, 11
Santa Ana (wind), 99
Satellites, weather, 7
  TIROS, 38-39, 163
Sea
  atmospheric interaction with, 23
  stable temperature of, 89-90
Sea breezes, 93-94
Seismographic detection of hurricanes, 66-70
Shakespeare, William, forecasting in works of, 103, 104
Ships
  infrared identification of, 149-50
  weather information to, 164, 167-68
  weather reports from, 163
Shoho (aircraft carrier), 12
Siberia, circulation over, 92-93
Silver Hill, Jamaica, 62
Silver iodide, 197, 216
Skyhooks (constant-altitude balloons), 46-51
Smog, inversions and, 131
Sniperscope (snooperscope), 149
Snowfall
  long-term changes in, 78
  measurement of, 171
Snow-removal services, forecasting for, 19-20
Solar energy, 5, 22
  nature of surface area and, 89-90
  temperature changes and, 85-87
Sound, weather lore and travel of, 109-112
Spee, Vice Adm. Graf Maximilian von, 11
Squall line, 119
Stability, *see* Atmospheric stability
State Department, U.S., 53
Stationary fronts, 123-24
Strategic Air Command, 53-54
Stratocumulus clouds, described, 184-185
Stratus clouds, described, 185
Sturdee, Vice Adm. Sir Doveton, 11
Sublimation nuclei, 193-95
Submarines, radar and, 25-26
Sun
  in weather lore, 103-4
  See also Solar energy
Supersaturated air, 191-92
Swell from hurricanes, 65-70
Symbols for weather analysis, 124

Tailored forecasts, 19-21
Teletypewriter reporting of data, 159-163
Temperature
  evaporation of water and, 202-3
  in global circulation, 90-92
  of land vs. ocean, 89-90, 93-94
  local variations in, 173-74
  long-term changes in, 77-78, 81-86
  measurement of, 174-77
  radiosonde observations of, 42-44
  rise and fall of air and, 127-30, 191
  in weather lore, 108
Temperature inversions, 131-33
Tennessee, U.S.S., 2
Theodolites, 41
Thermometers, 174-77
Thunderstorms
  cold fronts and, 119

control of, 223
orographic, 130, 222
on radar, 31-36
in warm fronts, 122
TIROS, 38-39, 163
Tornadoes, 119
control of, 223-24
described, 55-57
increase in number of, 80
radar detection of, 35
Trade winds, 90
Trenton, Battle of, 13
Tropical air in formation of cold fronts, 5-7
Tropical rain, formation of, 201-4
Tropical rain belt, proposed elimination of, 215-16
Tropical storms, 58-60
See also Hurricanes
Turbulence, clean-air, 136
Typhoons, *see* Hurricanes

U-boats, radar and, 25-26
UFO's, balloons as, 51
Utilities, tailored forecasts for, 20

Valley wind, 94-95
Venus and Adonis (Shakespeare), 103
Virgil, 103
Visibility, determination of, 147-49
Volcanic eruptions and temperature changes, 84-85
Von Braun, Werner, 213

Warm fronts
clouds of, 183-84
described, 121-22
on radar, 30
travel of sound and, 111-12
in weather lore, 106-7
Weather, *see specific topics*
Weather Bureau, U.S., 32, 72, 102, 125, 216, 223
Weather stations
automatic floating, 72-75
charting reports from, 161
instrument shelters of, 169-71
relocation of, 171
See also Observations
West Virginia, U.S.S., 2
Westerlies, 92
White Sands Proving Ground, 54
Willy-willies, *see* Hurricanes
Wind scale, 59
Windbreaks as weather control, 190
Winds, 89-100
"backing" and "veering" of, 108
global circulation of, 90-92
in hurricanes, 56, 64, 71
local circulation of, 92-100
measurement of
at ground stations, 173
by pilot balloons, 41-42
by radar on balloons, 42-44
reporting of, 163
in tornadoes, 56
in weather lore, 108-9
World Meteorological Organization, 158, 162, 172
World War I, sounds of battle in, 109-111
World War II
floating stations developed in, 75
influence of weather on
Coral Sea, 12
Enterprise raid, 1-10, 11
Guadalcanal, 12-13
Rabaul attacks, 13-16
Pearl Harbor attack, 2-4
radar in, 25-26, 113

Yorktown, U.S.S., 12

Zonda, 95